Houghton Mifflin

Daily Routines and Practice

Student Book

- Daily Routines
- Practice
- Looking Ahead Activities

GRADE

3

Visit **Education Place®**
www.eduplace.com/kids

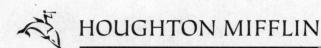

HOUGHTON MIFFLIN   BOSTON

Printed in the U.S.A.

ISBN 10: 0-618-95998-X
ISBN 13: 978-0-618-95998-3

        16 17 0982 15 14 13
4500418268

Hands On: Model Numbers

Problem of the Day ———————————————————— NS 1.1

What is the greatest whole number that can be made with the
digits: 4, 9, 3? Use each digit exactly once.

Number Sense Review ———————————————— Grade 2 KEY NS 1.1

Use Workmat 3 to write the number three hundred eight in
standard form.

Number of the Day ———————————————————— NS 1.1

8

Throughout the day, find ways in which the number 8 is used.

_____

_____

_____

Facts Practice ——————————————————— Grade 2 KEY NS 2.2

Add or subtract.

1. $4 - 1 =$ 2. $7 - 0 =$ 3. $9 + 1 =$

4. $1 - 0 =$ 5. $3 + 0 =$ 6. $6 + 1 =$

Hands On: Model Numbers

CA Standard
KEY NS 1.3

Write each number.

1.

_____

2.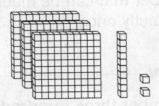

_____

3.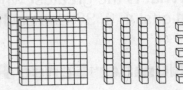

_____

4. 4 hundreds 6 tens 8 ones

_____

5. 8 hundreds 4 tens 7 ones

_____

6. 6 hundreds 5 tens

_____

7. 2 hundreds 9 ones

_____

Test Practice

Circle the letter of the correct answer.

8. What is the value of the digit 6 in the number 683?

   A 6

   B 60

   C 63

   D 600

9. Marianne added one 10-block to the model for a number. Which change could she have made?

   A 319 → 419

   B 683 → 684

   C 274 → 284

   D 406 → 426

Writing Math Suppose you model numbers with three digits, but you do not use any tens blocks. What digit must be in the standard form of every number you model? Give examples and explain.

_____

_____

Hands On: How Big is 1,000?

Problem of the Day ———————————————————————— KEY NS 1.5

Matt has 295 coins in his collection. Write the number of coins
Matt has in expanded form.

Algebra and Functions Review ——————————————— AF 1.3

If 15 ____ 9 = 6, what operational symbol goes in the blank?

Word of the Day ——————————————————————————— MR 2.3

greater

Use the word *greater* to describe something at school.

_____

_____

_____

Facts Practice ——————————————————————————— KEY NS 2.1

Find each sum.

1. 53 + 25   2. 68 + 16   3. 24 + 67

4. 45 + 44   5. 32 + 59   6. 76 + 18

Hands On: How Big Is 1,000?

CA Standards
NS 1.1, NS 1.0

Tell if each is *greater than*, *less than*, or *equal to* 1,000.

1. 8 boxes of 1,000 counters

   _____

2. 1 bag of 1,000 marbles

   _____

3. 5 trays of 100 cookies

   _____

4. 9 rolls of 100 stamps

   _____

5. 10 packs of 10 markers

   _____

6. 8 pages of 100 pictures

   _____

7. 10 boxes of 1,000 paint brushes

   _____

8. 10 boxes of 100 books

   _____

 Test Practice

Circle the letter of the correct answer.

9. Which is NOT equal to 1,000 peanuts?

   A 10 bags of 100 peanuts

   B 100 bags of 10 peanuts

   c 10 bags of 10 peanuts

   D 1 bag of 1,000 peanuts

10. Which best describes 12 dolls in each of 100 boxes?

    A equal to 100

    B less than 1,000

    c equal to 1,000

    D more than 1,000

Writing Math How is comparing 10 with 1 similar to comparing 1,000 with 100? Explain.

_____

_____

_____

Problem Solving: Number Patterns

Problem of the Day ————————————————————— KEY NS 1.3

Use these clues to find the year that Neil Armstrong became the
first man to walk on the moon.

• It has a 6 in the tens place.

• The hundreds and ones place have the largest possible digit.

• The thousands place is 5 less than the tens digit.

Number Sense Review ————————————————————— NS 1.1

Write 3,467 in word form.

_____

_____

Number of the Day ————————————————————— NS 1.1

5

Throughout the day, find ways in which the number 5 is used.

_____

_____

_____

Facts Practice ————————————————————— KEY NS 2.1

Find each difference.

1. $86 - 2$ 2. $35 - 8$ 3. $24 - 6$

4. $49 - 3$ 5. $92 - 7$ 6. $50 - 4$

Problem Solving: Number Patterns

CA Standards
MR 1.1, AF 2.2

Use a number pattern to solve each problem.

1. Sandy played in 4 soccer games in May, 7 soccer games in June, 10 soccer games in July, and 13 soccer games in August. If the pattern continues, in how many soccer games is Sandy likely to play in September?

   _____

2. Each soccer uniform has three red stripes running down the side. How many stripes are there on 9 uniforms?

   _____

3. Horus sold 4 tickets for the soccer tournament on Monday, 5 tickets on Tuesday, 7 tickets on Wednesday, and 10 tickets on Thursday. If the pattern continues, how many tickets is Horus likely to sell on Saturday?

   _____

4. Each player on the team had 3 friends come to see them play in the tournament. If there are 11 players on the team, how many friends came to watch them?

   _____

✓ Test Practice

Circle the letter of the correct answer.

5. Four lockers in the gym are numbered 15, 17, 19, and 21. If the pattern continues, what is the number of the next locker likely to be?

   A 22   C 23

   B 24   D 25

6. Each athletic shoe has 12 cleats on the bottom. How many cleats would there be on 2 pairs of athletic shoes?

   A 24   C 36

   B 48   D 60

Hands On: Compare Numbers

Problem of the Day
AF 2.2

The first four riders in a bicycle race are wearing the numbers 312, 315, 318, and 321. If this pattern continues, what is the number of the next rider likely to be?

Algebra and Functions Review
AF 2.2

Harry is painting flowers on some pictures. Each picture has 6 flowers painted on it. Use your whiteboard to determine how many flowers he will need to paint for 7 pictures.

Number of the Day
KEY NS 1.5

128

What are some ways you can show 128?

_____

_____

_____

Facts Practice
NS 2.0

Find each sum.

1. $3 + 9 + 4 =$ 2. $6 + 5 + 2 =$ 3. $2 + 8 + 7 =$

4. $5 + 5 + 5 =$ 5. $2 + 2 + 12 =$ 6. $7 + 4 + 7 =$

Name _____ Date _____

Hands On: Compare Numbers

CA Standards
NS 1.2, **KEY** NS 1.3

Compare. Write >, <, or = for each ◯.

1. 43 ◯ 41   2. 52 ◯ 72   3. 90 ◯ 87   4. 36 ◯ 36

5. 129 ◯ 93   6. 645 ◯ 645   7. 705 ◯ 792   8. 586 ◯ 986

9. 1,792 ◯ 1,792   10. 2,046 ◯ 2,135   11. 4,635 ◯ 3,287   12. 9,068 ◯ 9,014

Write = or ≠ for each ◯.

13. 15 + 3 ◯ 17   14. 13 + 4 ◯ 17   15. 30 + 8 ◯ 39

16. 200 + 9 ◯ 290   17. 300 + 90 ◯ 39   18. 100 + 20 ◯ 1,200

 **Test Practice**

Circle the letter of the correct answer.

19. Tickets were sold for four opera performances as follows: Thursday (845), Friday (1,042), Saturday (1,173) and Sunday (994). For which night were the greatest number of tickets sold?

    A Thursday   C Saturday

    B Friday   D Sunday

20. Which of the numbers shown below is less than 4,972?

    A 5,003

    B 4,969

    C 4,972

    D 4,981

Writing Math Suppose you are comparing two numbers that are greater than 1,000. You want to find the smaller of the numbers. How many pairs of digits might you have to compare before you have your answer? Explain.

_____

_____

_____

_____

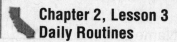
Round 2-Digit and 3-Digit Numbers

Problem of the Day ——————————————— NS 1.2

The table below shows the number of CDs some students have used during the school year.

Student	Number of CDs
Gerald	264
Anna	348
Suzi	235
Ben	257

Which student used more than 240 but less than 260 CDs?

Number Sense Review ——————————————— NS 1.2

On your white board, write 1,323; 965; and 990 in order from greatest to least.

Number of the Day ——————————————— NS 1.1

12

Why is the number 12 an important number?

_____

_____

Facts Practice ——————————————— NS 2.0

Skip count to find how many there are in all. Draw pictures or use counters if you need to.

1. 3 groups, 2 in each group   **2.** 8 groups, 2 in each group

3. 6 groups, 2 in each group   **4.** 2 groups, 2 in each group

5. 4 groups, 2 in each group   **6.** 9 groups, 2 in each group

Name _____ Date _____

Round 2-Digit and 3-Digit Numbers

CA Standards
NS 1.4, NS 1.0

**For each number, write the two tens the number is between.
Then round to the nearest ten.**

1. 28   **2.** 84   **3.** 682   **4.** 146

_____   _____   _____   _____

**For each number, write the two hundreds the number is
between. Then round to the nearest hundred.**

5. 505   **6.** 693   **7.** 872   **8.** 724

_____   _____   _____   _____

Round to the place of the underlined digit.

9. <u>1</u>6   **10.** <u>2</u>81   **11.** <u>6</u>57   **12.** 7<u>3</u>5

_____   _____   _____   _____

Test Practice

Circle the letter of the correct answer.

13. Which number rounds to 500 when
rounded to the nearest ten?

  A 491   **C** 508

  B 496   **D** 510

14. Which pair shows a number
and that number rounded to the
underlined digit?

  A <u>1</u>28 130   **C** <u>5</u>91 590

  B 3<u>5</u>2 400   **D** <u>6</u>63 700

Writing Math A number is rounded to the nearest 100.
What is the greatest possible difference between the original
number and the rounded number? Explain and give an example.

_____

_____

Round 4-Digit Numbers

Problem of the Day ———————————————— NS 1.4

The number of people at a concert rounded to the nearest
hundred is 500. What are the greatest and the least possible
number of people who could have been at the concert?

Number Sense Review ———————————————— NS 1.4

What is 187 rounded to the nearest ten and nearest hundred?

Number of the Day ———————————————— KEY

1,000

What are some ways you can show 1,000?

_____

_____

_____

Facts Practice ———————————————— NS 2.0

**Skip count to find how many there are in all. Draw pictures or
use counters if you need to.**

1. 2 groups, 5 in each group

2. 9 groups, 5 in each group

3. 7 groups, 5 in each group

4. 6 groups, 5 in each group

5. 3 groups, 5 in each group

6. 4 groups, 5 in each group

Name _____ Date _____

Round 4-Digit Numbers

CA Standards
NS 1.4, NS 1.0

Round to the place of the underlined digit.

1. 1,<u>6</u>75 _____

2. 2,3<u>8</u>1 _____

3. <u>1</u>,613 _____

4. <u>3</u>,406 _____

5. 4,5<u>0</u>9 _____

6. <u>3</u>,734 _____

7. 4<u>8</u>1 _____

8. 8,<u>1</u>13 _____

9. <u>6</u>02 _____

10. 5,<u>4</u>07 _____

11. 3<u>8</u>6 _____

12. 2,2<u>7</u>3 _____

13. <u>6</u>,510 _____

14. 3,<u>7</u>82 _____

15. 8,<u>3</u>08 _____

✓ Test Practice

Circle the letter of the correct answer.

16. Which number does **not** round to 6,000 when rounded to the nearest thousand?

   A 5,622

   B 6,023

   C 6,503

   D 6,499

17. Which number rounds to the same number whether it is rounded to the nearest ten, nearest hundred, or nearest thousand?

   A 1,899

   B 2,989

   C 5,014

   D 6,996

 Writing Math When you round a number to the nearest thousand, the hundreds, tens, and ones digits become zero. Shouldn't that mean that the rounded number is always less than the original number? Explain.

_____

_____

_____

_____

Problem Solving: Field Trip

Problem of the Day ————————————————————— NS 1.4

The number of students graduating from a university rounded
to the nearest thousand is 2,000. What are the greatest and the
least possible number of students who could be graduating?

Mathematical Reasoning Review ————————————— MR 2.3

Which is greater, $6,481 rounded to the nearest hundred or the
nearest thousand?

Word of the Day ———————————————————————— MR 2.3

skills

Identify three skills you have.

_____

_____

_____

Facts Practice ———————————————————————————— NS 2.0

**Tell the number of times you can subtract. Draw pictures or
use counters if you need to.**

1. a group of 5 from 10

2. a group of 2 from 12

3. a group of 4 from 20

4. a group of 6 from 18

5. a group of 10 from 30

6. a group of 3 from 12

Equations and Inequalities

Problem of the Day ———————————————— NS 2.0

Last year Dr. Smith vaccinated 365 children. This year she vaccinated 237 children. Without finding the sum, can you predict whether regrouping will be needed once or twice or not at all? Explain how you know.

Mathematical Reasoning Review ———————— MR 2.3

Explain why 563 + 274 does not equal 737. What is the correct sum?

Number of the Day ———————————————— KEY

12

On your whiteboard, write two different expressions that equal 12. Then write an equality using the two expressions.

_____

_____

_____

Facts Practice ———————————————————— NS 2.0

Subtract.

1. 8 − 2   2. 5 − 3   3. 10 − 6

4. 7 − 4   5. 9 − 4

Equations and Inequalities

CA Standard
KEY AF 1.1

Write $>$, $<$, or $=$ in each ☐. Tell if the number sentence is an equation or an inequality.

1. $26 + 31$ ☐ $45 + 12$ **2.** $74 + 12$ ☐ $37 + 48$ **3.** $46 - 13$ ☐ $75 - 41$

_____   _____   _____

Write a number in the ☐ that makes the number sentence true.

4. $301 + 66 > 212 +$ ☐   **5.** ☐ $+ 149 = 400 + 104$ **6.** $33 + 66 <$ ☐ $+ 50$

Test Practice

Circle the letter of the correct answer.

7. Which number makes the number sentence true?

$27 + 48 >$ ☐ $+ 71$

   A 3   **C** 5

   B 4   **D** 6

8. Which sign makes the number sentence true?

$129 + 31$ ☐ $81 + 79$

   A $>$ **C** $=$

   B $<$ **D** $\neq$

Writing Math Explain how an equation and an inequality are different.

_____

_____

_____

Addition Properties

Problem of the Day AF 1.0

Taylor spent $35 on her admittance ticket and $14 to park. Darrel spent $28 on his admittance ticket and $20 to park. Did they spend an equal amount of money? Explain.

Algebra and Functions Review ——— KEY AF 1.1

Write an inequality, equality, or expression to show 18 plus 22 is less than 50.

Number of the Day NS 1.2

$32

What are some items that cost more and less than $32?

_____

_____

_____

Facts Practice ——— KEY AF 1.1

Write >, <, or = for each ⬭.

1. $3 + 5$ ⬭ $5 + 3$

2. $8 - 5$ ⬭ $6 + 3$

3. $6 + 6$ ⬭ $5 + 5$

4. $9 - 2$ ⬭ $8 - 2$

5. $15 - 5$ ⬭ $5 + 6$

Addition Properties

Find the sum.

1. $\begin{array}{r} 3 \\ 4 \\ +7 \\ \hline \end{array}$

2. $\begin{array}{r} 6 \\ 8 \\ +2 \\ \hline \end{array}$

3. $\begin{array}{r} 5 \\ 7 \\ +5 \\ \hline \end{array}$

4. $\begin{array}{r} 6 \\ 0 \\ +9 \\ \hline \end{array}$

5. $\begin{array}{r} 9 \\ 3 \\ +4 \\ \hline \end{array}$

6. $30 + 6 + 12 =$ _____

   $12 + 30 + 6 =$ _____

7. $17 + 0 + 33 =$ _____

   $0 + 33 + 17 =$ _____

8. $1 + 7 + (6 + 6) =$ _____

9. $(7 + 8) + 51 + 9 =$ _____

Test Practice

Circle the letter of the correct answer.

10. It rained on 3 days in June. It rained on 9 days in July and 7 days in August. How many days did it rain in June, July, and August together?

    A 16   c 19

    B 18   D 20

11. Which problem does NOT have a sum of 27?

    A $13 + 7 + 7$

    B $(5 + 9) + 11 + 2$

    c $0 + 27 + 0$

    D $(14 + 6) + (8 + 9)$

Writing Math It is easy to add $1 + 2 + 3 + 4 + 5 + 6 + 7 + 8 + 9$ if you make tens. Explain how. What is the sum?

_____

_____

_____

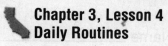
Column Addition

Problem of the Day ———————————————— AF 1.5

What property does the following equation show? What is the missing number?

$(15 + 13) + 7 = 15 + ($ ▮ $+ 7)$

Algebra and Functions Review ——————————— AF 1.2

If $4 + N > 10$, which of the following numbers could N be: 0, 1, 2, 3, 4, 5, 6, 7, 8, 9? Write the answer on your whiteboard.

Number of the Day ——————————————————— NS 1.1

20

Throughout the day, find quantities that add up to 20.

_____

_____

_____

Facts Practice ——————————————————————— NS 2.0

Multiply.

1. 6×1

2. 4×5

3. 7×2

4. 6×5

5. 5×3

Column Addition

CA Standards
KEY NS 2.1, MR 2.2

Add. Check by adding in a different order.

1.
```
   28
   15
 +36
```

2.
```
   45
   29
 +23
```

3.
```
   17
   56
 +21
```

4.
```
   38
   42
 +16
```

5.
```
  129
   57
 +12
```

6.
```
  597
  144
 +138
```

7.
```
   86
  203
 +514
```

8.
```
  103
  395
 +231
```

9. $35 + 27 + 14 =$

10. $124 + 36 + 93 + 45 =$

11. $476 + 29 + 43 =$

_____   _____   _____

Test Practice

Circle the letter of the correct answer.

12. The Rios family drove 16 miles to a museum. Then they drove 28 miles to visit a farm. Finally, they drove 34 miles to a camp. How many miles did the Rios family drive in all?

   A 44   C 68

   B 62   D 78

13. Forty-five students bought lunch on Monday. Eighteen students bought lunch on Tuesday. Thirty students bought lunch on Wednesday. How many lunches were bought over the three days?

   A 63   C 83

   B 75   D 93

Writing Math Explain why it is easy to add $204 + 36 + 10$ using mental math.

_____

_____

_____

Add Greater Numbers

Problem of the Day ——————————————— KEY NS 2.1

Fred was born 15 days before Ann. Jake was born 28 days before Fred. Lester was born 32 days before Jake. How many days before Ann was born was Lester born?

Mathematical Reasoning Review ——————— MR 2.6

How can you check that the sum of $125 + 38 + 75$ is 238?

Number of the Day ———————————————— NS 1.1

50

Why is the number 50 important?

_____

_____

_____

Facts Practice ———————————————————— KEY NS 2.1

Estimate each sum by rounding each addend to the nearest ten.

1. $28 + 34$ 2. $14 + 22$ 3. $76 + 11$

4. $54 + 47$ 5. $13 + 32$ 6. $98 + 67$

Name _____ Date _____

Add Greater Numbers

Find the sum.

1. $\begin{array}{r} 1,498 \\ +3,264 \\ \hline \end{array}$

2. $\begin{array}{r} 2,437 \\ +3,196 \\ \hline \end{array}$

3. $\begin{array}{r} 2,586 \\ +1,945 \\ \hline \end{array}$

4. $\begin{array}{r} 3,679 \\ +2,638 \\ \hline \end{array}$

5. $\begin{array}{r} 1,267 \\ +3,948 \\ \hline \end{array}$

6. $\begin{array}{r} 4,065 \\ +3,592 \\ \hline \end{array}$

7. $\begin{array}{r} 3,876 \\ +2,696 \\ \hline \end{array}$

8. $\begin{array}{r} 4,937 \\ +3,954 \\ \hline \end{array}$

Test Practice

Circle the letter of the correct answer.

9. Mount Washington in New Hampshire is 1,427 feet taller than Spruce Knob Mountain in West Virginia. Spruce Knob Mountain is 4,861 feet tall. How many feet tall is Mount Washington?

   A 3,436   C 7,288

   B 6,288   D 51,288

10. There are 1,376 little brown bats in one cave. There are 2,832 little brown bats in another cave. How many little brown bats are there in all?

   A 4,108   C 4,208

   B 4,199   D 4,218

Writing Math You know that 400 + 400 = 800. How can this help you find 2,400 + 3,400?

_____

_____

_____

_____

Problem Solving: Field Trip

Problem of the Day ———————————————— KEY NS 2.1

Last year West Elementary School collected 1,345 pair of glasses for charity. East Elementary collected 858. How many pair of glasses did the two schools collect last year in all?

Algebra and Functions Review ———————— AF 1.0

Would >, <, or = make the following number sentence true?

325 + 140 + 140 ⬭ 325 + 280

Word of the Day ———————————————————— NS 2.0

regroup

Write three addition problems on your whiteboard for which you would need to regroup to add.

_____

_____

_____

Facts Practice ———————————————————— NS 2.6

True or false?

1. $24 \times 0 = 0$

2. $0 \times 3 = 3$

3. $3 \times 1 = 1$

4. $1 \times 8 = 8$

5. $0 \times 100 = 1,000$

Name _____ Date _____

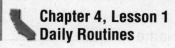
Hands On: Model Subtraction

Problem of the Day

A baby gorilla will stay with its mother until it is 36 months old. If one baby gorilla left its mother 18 months ago, how many months old is it now?

Number Sense Review

On workmat 1, write two 3-digit numbers. Circle the greater of the two numbers. Find the sum of the numbers.

Number of the Day

615

Write 615 in expanded form.

_____

_____

_____

Facts Practice

Subtract.

1. $8 - 5$

2. $5 - 2$

3. $12 - 6$

4. $6 - 4$

5. $12 - 4$

Name _____ Date _____

Hands On: Model Subtraction

Find each difference. Estimate to check.

1. 46
   −17

2. 87
   −38

3. 51
   −25

4. 86
   −17

5. 97
   −79

6. 322
   −15

7. 836
   −429

8. 437
   −218

9. 964
   −447

10. $683
    −$256

11. 433 − 115 =
_____

12. 262 − 134 =
_____

13. 692 − 267 =
_____

14. $721 − $707 =
_____

15. $952 − $436 =
_____

16. 336 − 219 =
_____

17. 792 − 424 =
_____

18. $837 − $306 =
_____

Test Practice

Circle the letter of the correct answer.

19. 842 − 237 =

   A 605

   B 609

   C 615

   D 619

20. Look at the number sentence below.

   125 − ☐ = 71

   Which number will make the
   number sentence true?

   A 50   C 54

   B 51   D 56

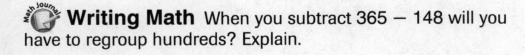 **Writing Math** When you subtract 365 − 148 will you
have to regroup hundreds? Explain.

_____

_____

_____

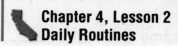
Hands On: Subtract with Regrouping

Problem of the Day KEY NS 2.1

Ms. Ortiz is driving a distance of 833 miles to her grandmother's house. The first day she drives 419 miles. About how many more miles must she drive the second day to reach her grandmother's house?

Number Sense Review KEY NS 2.1

Use base ten blocks to model 62 – 37.

Number of the Day KEY NS 2.1

45

Throughout the day, find numbers to subtract from 45.

_____

_____

_____

Facts Practice KEY NS 2.4

Multiply.

1. 8×8

2. 7×7

3. 6×6

4. 5×5

5. 4×4

Name _____ Date _____

Hands On: Subtract with Regrouping

Subtract. Check using addition.

1. 726
    −391

2. 429
    −381

3. 851
    −364

4. 671
    −202

5. 365
    −132

6. 241
    −168

7. 562
    −407

8. 672
    −273

9. 216
    −143

10. 946
    −797

11. 448
    −192

12. 562
    −175

13. 481
    −289

14. 561
    −116

15. 636
    −237

16. $217 - 183 =$ _____

17. $572 - 291 =$ _____

18. $911 - 422 =$ _____

 Test Practice

Circle the letter of the correct answer.

19. Which number is 103 less than 624?

    A 511

    B 515

    C 521

    D 524

20. What is the missing digit?

    4, ■14
    − 273
    4,641

    A 6

    B 7

    C 8

    D 9

 Writing Math When you do the subtraction shown on the right, how many times do you have to regroup? Explain.

3,231
− 743

_____

_____

Subtract Greater Numbers

Problem of the Day —————————————————— KEY **NS 2.1**

There are 632 people at the school play. Of those, 367 are
adults. How many children are at the play?

Number Sense Review —————————————————— KEY **NS 2.1**

**On your whiteboard, subtract 781 – 315. Show how to check
your answer.**

Number of the Day —————————————————— NS 1.0

0

Record numbers you hear or see today that have a 0 in the ones,
tens, and hundreds place.

_____

_____

_____

Facts Practice —————————————————— NS 2.0

Divide.

1. $6 \div 2$ 2. $10 \div 2$ 3. $8 \div 2$

4. $18 \div 2$ 5. $12 \div 2$

Subtract Greater Numbers

CA Standard
KEY NS 2.1

Find each difference.

1.   5,737
    −2,565

2.   8,683
    −5,837

3.   6,398
    −2,520

4.   7,717
    −3,556

5.   8,647
    −6,488

6.   3,546
    −3,253

7.   9,428
    −5,149

8.   8,861
    −6,675

9.   7,896
    −5,603

10.   2,738
    −1,466

11.   4,635
    −2,829

12.   5,768
    −2,846

13. $7,467 - 3,801 =$

14. $4,163 - 1,288 =$

15. $5,382 - 4,414 =$

Test Practice

Circle the letter of the correct answer.

16. Which number is the difference
    between 3,214 and 1,023?

    A 1,191

    B 2,191

    C 2,197

    D 2,291

17. What is the missing digit?

    4,837
    −4,1■9
    ─────
    648

    A 6

    B 7

    C 8

    D 9

 Writing Math When you do the subtraction shown on
the right, you regroup 1 thousand to 10 hundreds. Does that give
you 11 hundreds? Explain.

    4,126
    −2,487

_____

Subtract Across Zeros

Problem of the Day —————————————————— KEY NS 2.1

There were 1,359 people in the stadium on Friday. On Saturday, there were 3,216 people. How many more people were there in the stadium on Saturday?

Number Sense Review —————————————————— NS 1.1

Use your whiteboard to write each number in standard form.

1. nine thousand, five hundred twenty-one

2. six thousand, nine hundred two

Number of the Day —————————————————— KEY NS 1.5

400

What are some ways you can show 400?

_____

_____

_____

Facts Practice —————————————————— KEY NS 2.1

Add.

1. $34 + 25$

2. $69 - 31$

3. $19 + 17$

4. $53 - 13$

5. $51 + 34$

6. $85 - 73$

Name _____ Date _____

Subtract with Regrouping

CA Standard
KEY NS 2.1

Subtract. Check by adding or estimating.

1. 740
   −518

2. 600
   −358

3. 4,406
   −2,177

4. 900
   −535

5. 307
   −124

6. 860
   −424

7. 308
   −263

8. 8,007
   −6,352

9. 500
   −147

10. 300
    −162

11. 407 − 186 =

12. 5,500 − 3,217 =

13. 200 − 156 =

14. 9,002 − 2,890 =

15. 808 − 211 =

16. 308 − 104 =

17. 310 − 102 =

18. 502 − 117 =

19. 6,709 − 3,478 =

Test Practice

Circle the letter of the correct answer.

20. 8,000 − 4,261 =

    A 3,739   C 4,841

    B 3,839   D 4,849

21. Sam has 697 marbles. After receiving more marbles from a friend, Sam has 1,000 marbles. How many marbles did Sam receive?

    A 303   C 313

    B 307   D 413

Writing Math How is regrouping to find 304 − 169 different from regrouping to find 324 − 169?

_____

_____

_____

_____

Estimate Sums and Differences

Problem of the Day —————————————————— NS 2.0

There are 307 turkeys available to purchase for Thanksgiving.
If 219 are purchased, how many are still for sale?

Mathematical Reasoning Review ——————————— MR 2.6

Why is 395 not a reasonable answer for 1,000 − 405? What is
the difference?

Word of the Day ————————————————————— MR 2.3

reasonable

What might be *reasonable* to wear if it is 85°F outside?

_____

_____

_____

Facts Practice ——————————————————— KEY NS 2.1

Subtract.

1. 300 − 5

2. 100 − 2

3. 450 − 5

4. 500 − 75

5. 100 − 9

6. 600 − 60

Estimate Sums and Differences

CA Standards
NS 1.4, KEY NS 2.1

Estimate the sum or difference by rounding each number to the greatest place.

1.
$$84$$
$$-51$$

2.
$$92$$
$$-44$$

3.
$$32$$
$$+16$$

4.
$$517$$
$$+363$$

5.
$$836$$
$$-287$$

6.
$$334$$
$$-232$$

7. $632 + $221

8. $402 - $112

9. 289 + 122

Test Practice

Circle the letter of the correct answer.

10. Which is the best estimate for the difference of 893 and 221?

    A 600

    B 700

    C 800

    D 900

11. Amy did her math homework in 52 minutes. Her science homework took 47 minutes. Her brother did his homework in 30 minutes. About how much longer did Amy spend doing her homework than her brother?

    A 60 minutes   C 70 minutes

    B 90 minutes   D 100 minutes

Writing Math Ken is rounding 541 to the greatest place using a number line. He draws a number line that goes from 500 to 600. Why does he choose these two numbers?

_____

_____

Problem Solving: Estimate or Exact Amount?

Problem of the Day ———————————————————— NS 1.4

There are 632 people at the school play on Saturday. There are 367 people at the school play on Sunday. About how many people are at the play these two days?

Number Sense Review ———————————————————— NS 1.4

On your whiteboard, show how to estimate 399 + 147. Draw a number line as needed.

Number of the Day ———————————————————— KEY NS 1.5

500

What are some ways to show 500?

_____

_____

_____

Facts Practice ———————————————————————— NS 2.0

Multiply.

1. 6 × 1

2. 4 × 5

3. 7 × 2

4. 6 × 5

5. 5 × 3

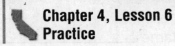
Problem Solving: Estimate or Exact Amount?

CA Standards
MR 2.5, MR 2.4

Use an estimate or exact answer to solve each problem. Then tell which method you used.

1. A matinee ticket to the movies is $3.75. Can Ralph buy 4 tickets if he has only $15? What change will he get back?

_____

_____

2. The first complete show of the movie begins at 1:10. The second show begins at 3:45. About how long is it between the two showings?

_____

3. Debbie's family drove to the state capital. The trip was 64 miles one way. They drove 22 miles and stopped for gas. How many more miles did Debbie's family have to drive to get to the capital?

_____

✔ Test Practice

Circle the letter of the correct answer.

4. Mike hiked 17 miles one day and 21 miles the next day. About how many miles did he hike both days?

   A 20 miles   c 30 miles

   B 35 miles   D 40 miles

5. It is 29 miles from Bridgetown to Grand City and 43 miles from Grand City to Mapleton. How far is it from Bridgetown to Mapleton?

   A 70 miles   c 72 miles

   B 80 miles   D 83 miles

Writing Math Carol estimated 35 + 49 and got one answer. Tim did the same problem and got an answer that was ten more than Carol's. Can they both be right? Explain.

_____

_____

Hands On: Model Multiplication

Problem of the Day

One round-trip train fare is $564. The student discount is $75.
What is the student price for a round trip ticket? Tell whether you
used an estimate or found an exact answer.

Mathematical Reasoning Review

A student ticket to the doll museum costs $2.25. Can April buy
4 tickets with a $10 bill? Explain how you got your answer.

Word of the Day

model

Use a sheet of paper to make or draw a model of a math
problem, an object, or a place of interest.

_____

_____

_____

Facts Practice

Subtract.

1. 28 − 22   2. 36 − 33   3. 45 − 36

4. 55 − 54   5. 105 − 103   6. 65 − 53

Hands On: Model Multiplication

CA Standards
KEY AF 1.1, MR 2.3

**Model each set with counters. Then write an addition sentence
and a multiplication sentence for each.**

1. 6 groups of 2

_____

_____

2. 2 groups of 5

_____

_____

3. 3 groups of 3

_____

_____

4. 4 groups of 4

_____

_____

Write a multiplication sentence for each.

5. $2 + 2 + 2 = 6$

_____

_____

6. $4 + 4 = 8$

_____

Test Practice

Circle the letter of the correct answer.

7. What is the correct multiplication
sentence for $5 + 5 + 5 = 15$?

   A $5 \times 2 = 10$ C $4 \times 3 = 12$

   B $3 \times 5 = 15$ D $5 \times 5 = 25$

8. Which multiplication sentence can
be used to represent 7 groups of 3?

   A 7×4 C 3×6

   B 3×7 D 7×7

Writing Math Sandy has 14 bottles. Describe how Sandy
can count the bottles by arranging them in an array.

_____

_____

Problem Solving: Field Trip

Problem of the Day

KEY NS 2.2

Dan has 8 boxes of chalk. There are 4 pieces of chalk in each box. How many pieces of chalk does Dan have?

Algebra and Functions Review

AF 2.2

Complete the table.

	Number of Cars	Number of Tires
1.	1	4
2.	2	
3.	3	
4.	4	
5.	5	
6.	6	

Number of the Day

KEY NS 2.2

4

Every time you hear the number 4 spoken, write a multiplication fact for 4 on your whiteboard.

Facts Practice

KEY NS 2.2

True or False?

1. $10 \times 2 = 20$

2. $4 \times 5 = 24$

3. $8 \times 2 = 14$

4. $4 \times 4 = 16$

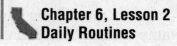
Multiply with 9

Problem of the Day ————————————————— NS 2.6

Brandon has 8 shirts. There are no logos on them. How many logos are on the 8 shirts in all?

Mathematical Reasoning Review ——————————— MR 2.3

Matthias has 1 bag of marbles with 8 marbles in each bag. Jane has 4 bags of marbles with 0 marbles in each bag. Who has more marbles, Matthias or Jane? On your whiteboard, write two number sentences to explain your answer.

Number of the Day ————————————————— NS 1.1

123

123 is a three-digit number whose digits are consecutive. What other three-digit numbers can you write using consecutive digits?

_____

_____

_____

Facts Practice ——————————————————— NS 2.0

Round each number to the greatest place. Then add.

1. 191 + 52

2. 11 + 88

3. $3.71 + $2.17

4. 309 + 637

5. 26 + 37

6. 45 + 54

Multiply with 9

CA Standards
KEY NS 2.2, AF 1.2

Multiply.

1. 9 × 7
2. 0 × 9
3. 1 × 9
4. 9 × 6
5. 9 × 8
6. 9 × 5

7. 4 × 9
8. 3 × 9
9. 10 × 9
10. 9 × 4
11. 9 × 2
12. 6 × 9

13. 9 × 3
14. 5 × 9
15. 7 × 9
16. 8 × 9
17. 9 × 9
18. 2 × 9

Test Practice

Circle the letter of the correct answer.

19. A quetzal (KET-sal) is a beautiful rain forest bird. There are 9 quetzal nests, with 4 eggs in each nest. How many eggs are there in all?

   A 13   c 27
   B 36   D 45

20. A coypu is a rain forest animal that looks like a big rat. There are 7 coypus and each has 9 babies. How many baby coypus are there in all?

   A 16   c 54
   B 63   D 72

Writing Math Your brother is in second grade. He knows how to add, but he hasn't learned how to multiply. Explain how he can find the product of 9 × 4 using addition.

_____

_____

Square Arrays

Problem of the Day ———————————————————————— NS 2.0

Oscar has 3 piles of magazines. There are 9 magazines in each pile. How many magazines does Oscar have?

Algebra and Functions Review ——————————————— AF 1.2

On your whiteboard, write the numbers, 0–10, that make $4 \times 9 > 5 \times$ ▨ true.

Number of the Day ———————————————————————— NS 2.0

25

Write all the whole number multiplication sentences that have a product of 25.

_____

_____

_____

Facts Practice ————————————————————————————— NS 2.6

Multiply.

1. 8×0

2. 1×5

3. 0×15

4. 535×1

5. $1,025 \times 0$

Name _____ Date _____

Square Arrays

Draw an array to find the product. Use grid paper.

1. $6 \times 6 =$ _____   2. $3 \times 3 =$ _____   3. $9 \times 9 =$ _____

4. $7 \times 7 =$ _____   5. $4 \times 4 =$ _____   6. $2 \times 2 =$ _____

7. $8 \times 8 =$ _____   8. $5 \times 5 =$ _____   9. $10 \times 10 =$ _____

Test Practice

Circle the letter of the correct answer.

10. Bryan put his rock collection in 6 rows, with 6 rocks in each row. How many rocks are in Bryan's collection?

   A 12   C 30
   B 36   D 66

11. Sam has 55 stamps in his collection. How many more stamps does he need to make a square number?

   A 0   C 6
   B 9   D 11

Writing Math How can you use an array to help you multiply 3×4?

_____

Problem Solving: Multistep Problems

Problem of the Day ———————————————— KEY

There are 3 park rangers. Each ranger takes 8 boy scouts on a hike. How many boy scouts is this?

Algebra and Functions Review ———————————— AF 1.5

If $12 \times 5 \times 1{,}001 = 60{,}060$, then what is $5 \times 12 \times 1{,}001$?

Number of the Day ——————————————————— KEY

16

On your white board, write all the multiplication facts having a product of 16. Circle the fact that tells you 16 is a square number.

_____

_____

_____

Facts Practice ————————————————————— KEY NS 2.1

Add.

1. $43 + 31$

2. $17 + 25$

3. $23 + 36$

4. $50 + 32$

5. $24 + 13$

Problem Solving: Multistep Problems

CA Standards
MR 1.2, NS 2.8

Use multiple steps to solve each problem.

1. Kaya pasted 3 rows of photos on each of 5 pages of her scrapbook. She put 2 photos in each row. How many photos are in Kaya's scrapbook?

   _____

2. John's vacation scrapbook has 2 times as many pages as his school scrapbook. There are 6 pages in John's school scrapbook. How many pages are in both of John's scrapbooks combined?

   _____

Test Practice

Circle the letter of the correct answer.

3. Members of the Scrapbook Club meet 2 days a week for 2 hours each day. How many hours will they meet in 6 weeks?

   A 12 hours

   B 18 hours

   C 20 hours

   D 24 hours

4. Kyle has 3 scrapbooks. Robin has 3 times as many scrapbooks as Kyle has. How many scrapbooks do Kyle and Robin have combined?

   A 12 scrapbooks

   B 9 scrapbooks

   C 13 scrapbooks

   D 30 scrapbooks

 **Writing Math** What words or phrases in problem 2 can help you figure out which operations to use to get the correct answer?

_____

_____

Hands On: Use a Multiplication Table

Problem of the Day ———————————————— NS 2.8

Heidi counted 2 roses on a rose bush. André counted 4 times as many roses on another rose bush. What was the total number of roses the two friends counted?

Number Sense Review ———————————————— NS 2.8

Ann was born 17 years before 1971. How old was Ann in 2001?

Number of the Day ———————————————— NS 1.1

100

Why is the number 100 important?

_____

_____

Facts Practice ———————————————— KEY NS 2.1

Subtract.

1. 562 − 27   **2.** 3,719 − 2,845

3. 3,215 − 2,876   **4.** 874 − 535

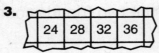
Hands On: Use a Multiplication Table

CA Standard
KEY NS 2.2

Below are parts of a multiplication table. In which row or column is the part found?

1. | 8 | 10 | 12 | 14 |

2.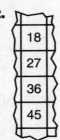

| 18 |
| 27 |
| 36 |
| 45 |

3. | 24 | 28 | 32 | 36 |

_____ _____ _____

Write *true* or *false* for each statement. Give examples to support your answers

4. The products in the row for 6 are double the products in the row for 3.

_____

5. The product 16 appears one time in the multiplication table.

_____

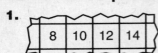 **Test Practice**

Circle the letter of the correct answer.

6. Which digits are in the ones place of a number multiplied by 5?

   A 0 or 1   C 0 or 5

   B 2 or 5   D 2 or 10

7. What is true about all numbers multiplied by 4?

   A They are even.   C They end in 4.

   B They are odd.   D They are square numbers.

Writing Math How could you use the products in the column for 1 to help you find the products in the column for 10? Explain.

_____

_____

Use What You Know to Multiply with 6, 7, and 8

Problem of the Day ——————————————— KEY NS 2.2

Mrs. Quan bought tickets for the 5 members of her family to attend a band concert. If each ticket costs $10, how much did Mrs. Quan pay in all?

Mathematical Reasoning Review ——————— MR 3.3

Look at a multiplication table. If you double the products in the row for 3, you get the products for 6. What will happen if you double the products for 4?

Number of the Day ——————————————— NS 1.1

11

Identify situations throughout the school day that involve the number 11.

_____

_____

_____

Facts Practice ——————————————————— KEY NS 2.2

Multiply.

1. 4×8 2. 8×8 3. 4×6

4. 8×6 5. 4×2 6. 8×2

Multiply with 6, 7, and 8

CA Standards
KEY NS 2.2, AF 1.5

Multiply.

1. $\begin{array}{r} 6 \\ \times 8 \\ \hline \end{array}$

2. $\begin{array}{r} 9 \\ \times 6 \\ \hline \end{array}$

3. $\begin{array}{r} 5 \\ \times 7 \\ \hline \end{array}$

4. $\begin{array}{r} 8 \\ \times 7 \\ \hline \end{array}$

5. $\begin{array}{r} 6 \\ \times 6 \\ \hline \end{array}$

6. $\begin{array}{r} 7 \\ \times 6 \\ \hline \end{array}$

7. $\begin{array}{r} 8 \\ \times 9 \\ \hline \end{array}$

8. $\begin{array}{r} 7 \\ \times 3 \\ \hline \end{array}$

9. $\begin{array}{r} 7 \\ \times 8 \\ \hline \end{array}$

10. $\begin{array}{r} 6 \\ \times 7 \\ \hline \end{array}$

11. $\begin{array}{r} 5 \\ \times 6 \\ \hline \end{array}$

12. $\begin{array}{r} 8 \\ \times 8 \\ \hline \end{array}$

13. $\begin{array}{r} 8 \\ \times 6 \\ \hline \end{array}$

14. $\begin{array}{r} 7 \\ \times 7 \\ \hline \end{array}$

Test Practice

Circle the letter of the correct answer.

15. Ms. Hanson bought 7 packs of colored pencils. Each pack had 9 pencils. How many pencils were there in all?

    A 54   **B** 56   **C** 63   **D** 64

16. Mason filled 6 vases with flowers. He put 8 flowers in each vase. How many flowers did Mason use in all?

    A 36   **B** 48   **C** 54   **D** 63

Writing Math Look at problem 16 above. If Mason had put 6 flowers in each of 8 vases, would he have used more flowers, fewer flowers, or the same number of flowers? Explain.

_____

_____

_____

Practice Multiplying by 6, 7, and 8

Problem of the Day ——————————————————— KEY NS 2.2

Josie buys 6 bags of grapefruit. Each bag contains 8 grapefruit. How many grapefruit did Josie buy?

Algebra and Functions Review ——————————— AF 1.5

If $94 \times 99 = 9{,}306$, then what does 99×94 equal?

Word of the Day ——————————————————————— MR 2.3

Table

Give reasons why Learning Tool 12, the multiplication table, is a table.

_____

_____

_____

Facts Practice ——————————————————————— KEY NS 2.1

Subtract.

1. $305 - 247$

2. $5{,}732 - 4{,}228$

3. $6{,}000 - 1{,}009$

4. $4{,}025 - 413$

Practice Multiplying with 6, 7, and 8

CA Standards
KEY NS 2.2, AF 1.5

Find the product.

1. $\begin{array}{r} 7 \\ \times 4 \\ \hline \end{array}$
2. $\begin{array}{r} 8 \\ \times 6 \\ \hline \end{array}$
3. $\begin{array}{r} 3 \\ \times 7 \\ \hline \end{array}$
4. $\begin{array}{r} 7 \\ \times 6 \\ \hline \end{array}$
5. $\begin{array}{r} 7 \\ \times 5 \\ \hline \end{array}$

6. $\begin{array}{r} 10 \\ \times 7 \\ \hline \end{array}$
7. $\begin{array}{r} 7 \\ \times 7 \\ \hline \end{array}$
8. $\begin{array}{r} 9 \\ \times 7 \\ \hline \end{array}$
9. $\begin{array}{r} 7 \\ \times 8 \\ \hline \end{array}$
10. $\begin{array}{r} 8 \\ \times 5 \\ \hline \end{array}$

11. $7 \times 3 =$ _____
12. $7 \times 10 =$ _____
13. $8 \times 8 =$ _____

14. $5 \times 7 =$ _____
15. $9 \times 8 =$ _____
16. $7 \times 4 =$ _____

Test Practice

Circle the letter of the correct answer.

17. Heather bought 9 packs of stamps. There are 6 stamps in each pack. How many stamps did Heather buy?

    A 15   B 42   C 48   D 54

18. Larry bought 7 packs of postcards. There are 8 cards in each pack. How many postcards did Larry buy?

    A 15   B 42   C 56   D 63

Writing Math How can you use skip counting to multiply 5×6? Explain.

_____

_____

_____

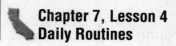
Use the Associative Property

Problem of the Day ———————————————— NS 2.0

Philip rode his bike 6 miles each day for 1 week. What is the total number of miles Philip rode his bike?

Number Sense Review ———————————————— NS 2.0

What must you add to 1,234 to get 4,567?

Number of the Day ———————————————— KEY

8

Throughout the day, find numbers that have the digit 8 in the ones place.

_____

_____

_____

Facts Practice ———————————————————— NS 1.4

Round each number to the nearest hundred.

1. 844

2. 1,538

3. 6,955

4. 4,872

Use the Associative Property

CA Standard
AF 1.5

Find the product. Multiply factors in parentheses first.

1. $(4 \times 2) \times 7 =$ _____

2. $11 \times (6 \times 0) =$ _____

3. $(1 \times 9) \times 5 =$ _____

4. $(2 \times 3) \times 8 =$ _____

5. $9 \times (3 \times 3) =$ _____

6. $(2 \times 5) \times 4 =$ _____

7. $7 \times (2 \times 3) =$ _____

8. $(2 \times 4) \times 8 =$ _____

9. $3 \times (8 \times 1) =$ _____

10. $(8 \times 1) \times 4 =$ _____

11. $(3 \times 3) \times 6 =$ _____

12. $5 \times (3 \times 2) =$ _____

 **Test Practice**

Circle the letter of the correct answer.

13. Three children each have 2 toy cars. Each car has 4 wheels. How many wheels are there in all?

   A 9   B 18   C 24   D 36

14. Five children each have 2 boxes of crayons. Each box holds 8 crayons. How many crayons are there in all?

   A 15   B 40   C 45   D 80

Writing Math Your friend says that the problem $5 \times 3 \times 3$ is too hard. He says he knows that 5×3 is 15, but he doesn't know how to multiply 15×3. Explain an easier way for your friend to find the product.

_____

_____

_____

Problem Solving: Guess and Check

Problem of the Day ———————————————— AF 1.5

If 6 × 7 = 42, then what is 7 × 6? And if 6 × 7 × 3 = 126, then what is 7 × 3 × 6?

Algebra and Functions Review ———————— AF 1.2

What number makes 8 + 8 = ▓▓▓ × 4 a true number sentence?

Word of the Day ———————————————————— MR 2.0

reasonable

Make three guesses today. Explain how you know you made a reasonable guess.

_____

_____

_____

Facts Practice ———————————————————— AF 1.5

Tell the property each number sentence represents.

1. (2 × 4) × 3 = 2 × (4 × 3)

2. 9 × 3 = 3 × 9

3. (8 + 5) + 15 = 8 + (5 + 15)

4. 45 + 18 = 18 + 45

Problem Solving: Guess and Check

CA Standards
MR 2.0, NS 2.0

Use the guess and check strategy to solve each problem.

1. The Jacksons have pet dogs named Beau and Max. Beau is 2 years older than Max. The sum of their ages is 16 years. How old is Beau? How old is Max?

   _____

2. Together, Misty and Keith caught 29 fish this summer. Keith caught 5 fewer fish than Misty. How many fish did Misty catch? How many fish did Keith catch?

   _____

3. The Nature Center has 50 reptiles and birds on exhibit. There are 20 more birds than reptiles. How many reptiles are on exhibit at the Nature Center? How many birds?

   _____

4. Koalas and sloths are very sleepy animals. Together, a koala and a sloth can sleep 42 hours a day. Suppose a koala sleeps 2 hours more than a sloth. How long does each animal sleep?

   _____

Test Practice

Circle the letter of the correct answer.

5. Rob and Linda did 20 hours of yard work this weekend. Linda did 4 more hours of work than Rob. How many hours did Rob do?

   A 8 hours
   B 10 hours
   C 12 hours
   D 6 hours

6. Max and Fernando together had 32 hits during the baseball season. Max had 6 fewer hits than Fernando. How many hits did Fernando have?

   A 13
   B 17
   C 19
   D 21

Writing Math If problem 3 above gave the fact that there were 35 birds on exhibit, would you need to guess and check? Explain your answer.

_____

_____

Hands On: Measure to the Nearest Inch

Problem of the Day ————————————— MR 2.0

Katie and Brian have a total of 60 CDs. Brian has 5 times as many CDs as Katie. How many CDs do they each have?

Number Sense Review ————————————— KEY

The light bulb was invented in 1879. The Hula hoop was invented in 1958. How many years after the light bulb was the Hula hoop invented?

Number of the Day ————————————— KEY

365

There are 365 days in 1 year. How many days are in 5 years?

_____

_____

_____

Facts Practice ————————————— NS 1.4

Round to the nearest ten, hundred, and thousand.

1. 547

2. 1,432

3. 6,891

4. 3,464

5. 5,555

Hands On: Measure to the Nearest Inch

**CA Standard
MG 1.1**

Estimate and then measure each object below to the nearest inch.

1.

_____

2.

_____

3.

_____

Use a ruler. Draw a line of each length.

4. 4 inches

5. 6 inches

Test Practice

Circle the letter of the correct answer.

6. Choose the best estimate.

A about 2 inches   c about 5 inches

B about 9 inches   d about 11 inches

7. Which object is most likely to be about 6 inches in length?

A paper clip   c fork

B egg   D suitcase

 Writing Math When Jacob measured the length of a pencil, he lined up one end of the pencil with the number 1 on the ruler. The number closest to the other end of the pencil was 6. Jacob says the pencil is 6 inches long. What's wrong?

_____

Convert Customary Units of Length

Problem of the Day ——————————————— MG 1.1

Belinda measured the length of a board. It measured exactly 9 inches. Then she cut the board in half. To the nearest inch, how long was each piece of board?

Algebra and Functions Review ——————— KEY

Ms. Farm bought 7 cartons of eggs. Each carton is packed with 12 eggs. Write a number sentence for the total number of eggs bought.

Number of the Day ——————————————— KEY

5,280

There are 5,280 feet in 1 mile. How do you write 5,280 in expanded notation?

_____

_____

Facts Practice ——————————————————— NS 1.4

Estimate each sum by rounding the addends to the greatest place value.

1. $463 + 278$ **2.** $291 + 542$ **3.** $615 + 108$

4. $470 + 236$ **5.** $237 + 382$ **6.** $128 + 754$

Convert Customary Units of Length

CA Standards
MG 1.4, MG 1.1

Circle the letter of the better estimate.

1. the distance across a city

   a. 5 miles   **b.** 5 feet

2. the width of a stamp

   a. 1 yard   **b.** 1 inch

3. the length of a table

   a. 3 feet   **b.** 3 miles

4. the height of a door

   a. 7 feet   **b.** 7 inches

Complete.

5. 12 ft = _____ yd

6. 3 ft = _____ in.

7. 2 yd = _____ ft

8. 24 in. = _____ ft

9. 9 ft = _____ yd

10. 1 ft = _____ in.

 **Test Practice**

Circle the letter of the correct answer.

11. Choose the measurement that is greater than 3 feet.

   A 1 yard   **c** 2 yards

   B 24 inches   **D** 36 inches

12. Which is the best estimate for the length of a basketball court?

   A 90 inches   **c** 90 feet

   B 10 feet   **D** 900 yards

Writing Math Which is less, 3 feet or 48 inches? Explain how you know.

_____

_____

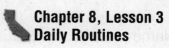
Hands On: Centimeters and Millimeters

Problem of the Day ———————————————— MG 1.4

Keesha has a necklace that measures 15 inches long. Karen
has a necklace that measures 1 foot 2 inches long. Who has the
longer necklace?

Number Sense Review ———————————— KEY NS 2.4

If Danielle walks 6 miles, how many feet does she walk? How
many yards does she walk?

Word of the Day ————————————————— MG 1.1

estimate

Give some examples of what lengths you might estimate during
the school day.

_____

_____

_____

Facts Practice ———————————————— KEY NS 2.2

Multiply.

1. 8×10 **2.** 10×2 **3.** 5×10

4. 10×4 **5.** 10×1 **6.** 6×10

Hands On: Centimeters and Millimeters

CA Standards
MG 1.1, MR 2.5

Estimate. Then measure to the nearest centimeter and the nearest millimeter.

1.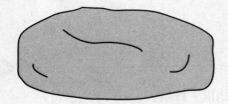

    _____

    _____

2. _____

    _____

Choose the better estimate.

3. length of a shoe
    20 cm or 20 mm

    _____

4. length of a paper clip
    3 cm or 3 mm

    _____

5. width of your wrist
    4 cm or 14 cm

    _____

6. width of a
    picture
    3 mm or 9 cm

    _____

7. width of notebook
    20 cm or 4 mm

    _____

8. width of a calculator
    3 cm or 10 cm

    _____

Test Practice

Circle the letter of the correct answer.

9. Which is the best estimate of the
    length of a soup spoon?

    A 16 cm   c 60 cm

    B 6 mm   D 60 mm

10. Which measure is closest to
    59 mm?

    A 50 mm   c 6 mm

    B 65 mm   D 6 cm

Writing Math Beth needs to measure the yarn. What is the length
of the yarn to the nearest centimeter? Explain how you found your answer.

_____

Convert Metric Units of Length

Problem of the Day ——————————— MG 1.1

Dana measured her desk using centimeters. Then she measured
the same length using millimeters. Which measure had the
greater number of units—the measure using centimeters or
millimeters?

Algebra and Functions Review ——————— KEY

There were 5 dogs on the grass and 2 dogs swimming in the
pond, which is greater than the 3 birds in the tree. Write an
inequality expression to match the story.

Number of the Day ——————————— MG 1.1

10

Measure 3 objects in centimeters. Multiply the centimeters by 10
to find the measure of the object in millimeters.

_____

_____

_____

Facts Practice ————————————— AF 1.2

Write the number that makes the equation true.

1. $6 + \boxed{} = 6$

2. $5 + 14 = 14 + \boxed{}$

3. $(32 + 18) + 12 = \boxed{} + (18 + 12)$

4. $0 + \boxed{} = 8$

5. $46 + 54 = \boxed{} + 54$

Convert Metric Units of Length

Choose the unit you would use to measure each.
Write *mm, cm, m,* or *km.*

1. length of a killer whale _____

2. distance from Africa to South America _____

3. thickness of a book cover _____

4. height of a drinking cup _____

Circle the letter of the better estimate.

5. height of a stack of 30 sheets of paper

   a. 2 mm   **b.** 2 m

6. distance for a 1-hour bike ride

   a. 800 m   **b.** 8 km

7. height of the tightrope in a circus

   a. 15 cm   **b.** 15 m

8. length of a person's nose

   a. 3 mm   **b.** 3 cm

 **Test Practice**

Circle the letter of the correct answer.

9. Which length is between 7 m and 9 m?

   A 80 cm   **c** 74 cm

   B 8 km   **D** 740 cm

10. What is the missing unit on this Canadian road sign?

   | Vancouver 85 □ |

   A mm   **c** m

   B cm   **D** km

Writing Math Why does converting from a longer metric unit of length to a shorter one require multiplication? Give an example and explain.

_____

_____

_____

Problem Solving: Field Trip

Problem of the Day ——————————————— MG 1.4

Taylor is running in a race that is 5 kilometers long. He has completed exactly one half of the race. How many meters has Taylor run so far?

Number Sense Review ——————————————— KEY NS 2.1

Maria spent $53 to buy two purses. The price of one purse was $11 greater than the price of the other purse. What were the prices of the two purses?

Word of the Day ——————————————— MR 2.3

strategy

Estimate these problems. Tell what strategy you used.

$213 + 562$

$26 + 53$

$115 + 432$

_____

_____

_____

Facts Practice ——————————————— KEY NS 2.2

Multiply.

1. 6×5 2. 4×8 3. 7×9

4. 3×5 5. 9×9 6. 8×6

Name _____ Date _____

Plane Figures

Problem of the Day —————————————————— MG 2.4

Alexis saw this sign at a shop.

SALE THIS WEEK

ON ALL HATS

How many letters on the sign have at least one right angle?

Algebra Review ————————————————— KEY

Which of the following is used to find out how many feet are in
6 yards?

A 6 + 3

B 6 ÷ 3

C 6 × 3

D 6 − 3

Word of the Day ————————————————— MG 2.4

right angle

Draw at least three figures that have right angles.

_____

_____

_____

Facts Practice ————————————————— KEY

Subtract.

1. 867 − 439   2. 1,642 − 864   3. 3,094 − 1,268

4. 8,763 − 3,678   5. 2,001 − 999

Plane Figures

Tell whether the figure is a polygon. If it is, write its name.

1.   2.   3.   4.

_____   _____   _____   _____

_____   _____   _____

Use the plane figures at the right to answer question.

5. Which figures have more than 3 angles?

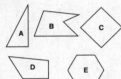

_____

 Test Practice

Circle the letter of the correct answer.

6. Travis drew a pentagon. Which figure did he draw?

A 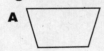   **C**

B   **D**

7. Flora drew the figure below. What is it called?

A quadrilateral   **c** octagon

B pentagon   **d** hexagon

Writing Math Min drew the figure. She says it is a polygon because it is closed and made up of line segments. Explain why Min's figure is not a polygon.

_____

_____

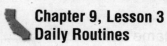
Hands On: Sort Triangles and Quadrilaterals

Problem of the Day
KEY MG 2.1

Bridget saw a stop sign on her way to school. Bridget told her friend, Amy, that it was an octagon. Amy said that it was a hexagon. Who is correct and why?

Geometry Review
KEY MG 2.1

Emma is making a quilt using pentagons. Which of these is a pentagon?

 A

 C

 B

D

Word of the Day
MR 2.3

sort

Sort these numbers. Describe your sort rule.

5   10   16   19   24   37   40

_____

_____

_____

Facts Practice
KEY NS 2.2

Multiply mentally.

1. 6×4 2. 4×2 3. 8×4

4. 4×5 5. 4×7 6. 9×4

Hands On: Sort Triangles and Quadrilaterals

CA Standards
KEY MG 2.2, **KEY** MG 2.3,

Sort the triangles and quadrilaterals. Write the letter(s).
Use a ruler to help you.

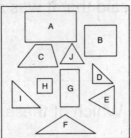

1. Which triangles have no right angles? _____

2. Which quadrilaterals have 1 pair of parallel sides? _____

3. Which quadrilaterals have 2 pairs of parallel sides? _____

4. Which triangles have all sides the same length? _____

5. Which triangles have 1 right angle? _____

6. Which quadrilaterals have all sides the same length? _____

Test Practice

Circle the letter of the correct answer.

7. Chee drew a triangle with all sides the same length. Which triangle did he draw?

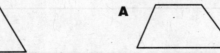

A   C

B   D

8. Jenna drew a quadrilateral with only 1 pair of parallel sides. Which quadrilateral did she draw?

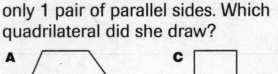

A   C

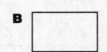

B   D

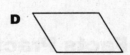

 Writing Math Ben drew this figure: □. Describe its angles and sides.

_____

_____

Triangles

Problem of the Day ——————————————— KEY MG 2.3

Chin drew a quadrilateral with four right angles. What are two possible quadrilaterals Chin drew?

Number Sense Review ——————————————— KEY NS 2.4

On Friday, the exhibit at the museum had 1,875 visitors. Four times as many visitors saw the exhibit on Saturday than on Friday. How many visitors saw the exhibit on Saturday?

Number of the Day ——————————————— NS 1.1

3

How many ways can you use the digits 1, 2, 4, or 0 to make the number 3?

_____

_____

_____

Facts Practice ——————————————— KEY NS 2.2

Multiply mentally.

1. 3×5 2. 6×4 3. 9×10

4. 4×3 5. 5×5 6. 8×4

Triangles

CA Standard
KEY MG 2.2

Name the triangle. Write *equilateral*, *isosceles*, *right*, or *scalene*. Triangles can have more than one name. Use a ruler.

1.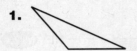

2.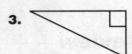

3.

4.

_____   _____   _____   _____

_____   _____   _____   _____

Test Practice

Circle the letter of the correct answer.

5. Ryan drew a scalene triangle. Which triangle did he draw?

A

B

C

D

6. Hilda drew a triangle with sides that are 10 cm, 10 cm, and 12 cm long. What kind of triangle did she draw?

A isosceles   C equilateral

B right   D scalene

Writing Math Some isosceles triangles are also right triangles. Can Hilda's triangle in problem 6 be a right triangle? Use a ruler and try to draw a right triangle with sides 10 cm, 10 cm, and 12 cm. Explain.

_____

_____

_____

Quadrilaterals

Problem of the Day ————————————————————— KEY MG 2.2

Jennifer drew a triangle with three unequal sides. What kind of triangle did she draw?

Number Sense Review ——————————————————— KEY NS 1.5

Jason has 1,643 pennies in his collection. Write this number in expanded form.

Number of the Day ————————————————————— NS 1.1

44

What are some ways you can show 44?

_____

_____

Facts Practice ——————————————————————— KEY NS 2.2

Multiply mentally.

1. 5×6 2. 3×5 3. 9×5

4. 1×5 5. 5×2 6. 7×5

Quadrilaterals

CA Standard
KEY MG 2.3

Tell whether the figure is a quadrilateral. If it has special names, write them.

1.

2.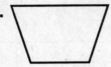

3.

4.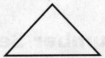

_____ _____ _____ _____

_____ _____ _____ _____

Test Practice

Circle the letter of the correct answer.

5. Molly drew a quadrilateral with opposite sides that are parallel. Which was **not** the figure Molly drew?

   A   C

   B   D

6. Juan drew a quadrilateral. It has 4 sides of equal length and 4 right angles. Which figure did he draw?

   A   C

   B   D

Writing Math How are a square and a rectangle alike? How are they different? Explain.

_____

_____

_____

_____

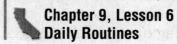
Problem Solving: Draw a Picture

Problem of the Day

Peter drew shapes in a pattern.

What is the special name of the quadrilateral that comes next in the pattern?

Geometry Review

Andrea drew a circle, triangle, pentagon, and hexagon. Which figure is not a polygon? Why?

Number of the Day

3

Draw 3 figures with four sides.

Facts Practice

Multiply.

1. 25×1 2. 15×0 3. 0×6

4. 9×1 5. 1×74 6. 39×0

Problem Solving: Draw a Picture

Draw a picture to solve each problem.

1. Nate cuts a board that is 54 inches long into 6 equal pieces. How long is each piece?

    _____

2. Erin is cutting a loaf of bread into 12 slices. What is the fewest number of cuts she can make?

    _____

3. There are 24 flowers planted in a flowerbed. The flowers are pink, yellow, white, and purple. Every fourth flower is pink. How many pink flowers are there?

    _____

4. Pete's mom buys 48 inches of ribbon. First she cuts the ribbon in half. Then she cuts each piece into 3 equal pieces. How many pieces of ribbon will she have then?

    _____

Test Practice

Circle the letter of the correct answer.

5. There are 3 wagons in a wagon train. Each wagon is 15 feet long. There are 5 feet between each wagon. What is the length of the wagon train?

    A 45 feet   **C** 50 feet

    B 55 feet   **D** 60 feet

6. Kayla has 4 triangles. If she joined them together with the four base sides facing each other, what shape will she form?

    A a diamond   **C** a star

    B a square   **D** a bigger triangle

Writing Math In problem 4 above, is there a piece of information that isn't necessary to the solution? If so, what is it?

_____

_____

Hands On: Explore Perimeter

Problem of the Day
MR 2.3

Katy is designing a rug. She wants equal rows of blue, green, and yellow. She wants the blue area to be 6 inches long. She wants to repeat the pattern 2 times. How long will her rug be?

Geometry Review
KEY MG 2.3

Juan drew a quadrilateral. It had 4 equal sides and 4 right angles. What is the name of the quadrilateral that Juan drew?

Number of the Day
NS 1.4

555

Round 555 to the nearest ten, hundred, thousand.

_____

_____

_____

Facts Practice

Estimate to the greatest place value.

1. $46 + 23$

2. $163 + 92$

3. $469 + 249$

4. $1,264 + 4,621$

5. $6,721 + 2,839$

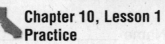
Hands On: Explore Perimeter

CA Standards
KEY MG 1.3, MG 1.1

Complete the chart below. Trace a face of each object. Then estimate the perimeter of the face. Record your estimates. Then measure the perimeter using paper clips, toothpicks, and a ruler.

	Object	Object Used to Measure	Estimate	Measurement
1.	science book	paper clips		
		toothpicks		
		ruler		
2.	3-ring binder	paper clips		
		toothpicks		
		ruler		
3.	magazine	paper clips		
		toothpicks		
		ruler		

4. Which object has the greatest perimeter? The least? _____

✓ Test Practice

5. Choose the best estimate of the perimeter of the top of a table.

   A 2 inches   c 1,000 inches

   B 90 inches   D 17,000 inches

6. Choose the most likely estimate of the length of a kitchen table.

   A 1 foot   c 4 feet

   B 14 feet   D 200 feet

Writing Math Jessique measured the perimeter of her hand with a piece of string. She is trying to decide which unit of length to use to record the length. Which unit should she choose: inches, yards, or feet? Explain.

Find Perimeter

Problem of the Day ————————————————————— MG 1.1

Jaime wants to make a frame for a painting. To measure the
perimeter, he runs a string around the perimeter of the painting.
What should he do next?

Geometry Review ———————————————————— KEY MG 2.2

Lynn drew a triangle with sides that are 10 cm, 10 cm, and
12 cm long. What kind of triangle did she draw?

Word of the Day ———————————————————— KEY MG 2.1

polygon

Draw 3 polygons on Workmat 1.

Facts Practice ———————————————————————— KEY NS 2.1

Add.

1. 20 + 32

2. 24 + 16

3. 10 + 9

4. 16 + 17

5. 12 + 12

Find Perimeter

CA Standards
KEY MG 1.3, MG 1.0

Find the perimeter of each figure.

1.

6 ft
5 ft   5 ft
3 ft

_____

2.

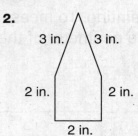

3 in. 3 in.
2 in.   2 in.
2 in.

_____

3.

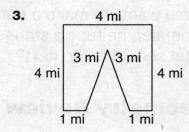

4 mi
3 mi 3 mi
4 mi   4 mi
1 mi   1 mi

_____

Measure the sides of each figure with a centimeter ruler. Then find the perimeter.

4.

_____

5.

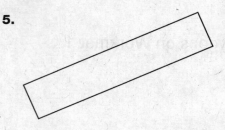

_____

Test Practice

6. The perimeter of a triangle is 26 centimeters. The length of one side is 9 centimeters. The length of another side is 7 centimeters. What is the length of the third side?

A 10 cm   C 12 cm
B 11 cm   D 13 cm

7. A rectangle has sides that measure 10 cm and 2 cm. What is the perimeter of the rectangle?

A 12 cm   C 20 cm
B 24 cm   D 104 cm

Writing Math The length of each side of a square is 8 inches. Explain how to find the perimeter of the square. What is the perimeter?

_____

Name _____ Date _____

Hands On: Explore Area

Problem of the Day ──────────────────── KEY

Gail's garden is shaped like a rectangle 15 feet long and 12 feet wide. What is the perimeter of the garden?

Algebra Review ──────────────────── KEY **AF 1.1**

Write a number sentence to find the perimeter of a triangle that has two sides that are each 40 inches long and one side 60 inches long.

Number of the Day ──────────────────── KEY **NS 2.2**

15

Write multiplication sentences so that the product is 15.

_____

_____

_____

Facts Practice ──────────────────── KEY

Multiply.

1. 6×6 **2.** 5×5 **3.** 3×3

4. 8×8 **5.** 4×4 **6.** 9×9

Name _____ Date _____

Hands On: Explore Area

**Estimate the area of each figure. Each
□ = 1 square unit.**

1.
_____

2.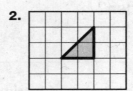
_____

3.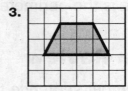
_____

4.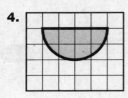
_____

5.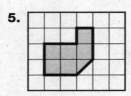
_____

6.
_____

7.
_____

8.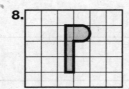
_____

9.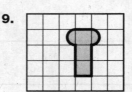
_____

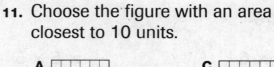 **Test Practice**

10. Choose the figure with an area of
about 2 square units.

A   C

B   D

11. Choose the figure with an area
closest to 10 units.

A   C

B   D

Writing Math Look at exercises 1 and 4. Is it easier to
estimate the area of a rectangle or a semi-circle? Explain.

Find Area

Problem of the Day ——————————————— KEY MG 1.2

Damen drew a triangle on grid paper. What is the area of the triangle Damen drew?

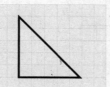

Each ▨ = 1 square unit.

Number Sense Review ——————————————— KEY NS 1.3

What is the value of the digit 3 in each number?

364

3,749

834

4,013

Word of the Day ——————————————— KEY MG 1.2

square unit

Draw a polygon on Workmat 6. Find the area in square units.

Facts Practice ——————————————— KEY NS 2.2

Multiply mentally.

1. 3×6 2. 8×3 3. 3×5

4. 9×3 5. 3×4 6. 3×7

Find Area

CA Standard
KEY MG 1.2

Find the area of each figure. Label your answer in square
units. Each □ or ⋮ = 1 square unit.

1.

_____

2.

_____

3.

_____

4.

_____

5.

_____

6.

_____

Test Practice

7. Choose the area of the figure.

A 2 square units   **c** 3 square
units

B $2\frac{1}{2}$ square units   **D** 4 square
units

8. Choose the area of the figure.

A 3 square
units   **c** 4 square
units

B $4\frac{1}{2}$ square
units   **D** 9 square
units

Writing Math MacKenzie is trying to determine the area of the shape
below. Explain how you know the area is 9 square units.

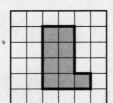

_____

_____

Problem Solving: Find a Pattern

Problem of the Day ———————————————— KEY MG 1.2

Stephen used a Geoboard and made a triangle. What is the area
of the triangle? Label your answer in square units.

Each $\vdots$ = 1 square unit.

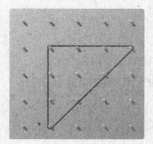

Measurement Review ———————————————— KEY MG 1.3

The length of a side of a square is 16 inches. What is the
perimeter of the square?

Word of the Day ———————————————————— AF 2.2

pattern

Describe the number of figure patterns you see during the school
day.

_____

_____

_____

Facts Practice ———————————————————— AF 2.2

Find the missing number.

1. 2, 4, _____, 8, 10, 12

2. 1, 3, 5, 7, _____, 11, 13, 15

3. 3, 6, 9, 12, _____, 18

4. 5, 10, 15, _____, 25, 30

Name _____ Date _____

Problem Solving: Find a Pattern

CA Standards
MR 1.1, AF 2.2

1. Maki made the pattern below using $\frac{1}{2}$-inch tiles.

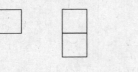

If he continued the pattern, what will the perimeter of the fourth figure be?

_____

2. This pattern was made using 1-inch tiles.

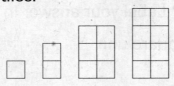

If the pattern is continued, which figure will have a perimeter of 24 inches?

_____

Test Practice

Circle the letter of the correct answer.

3. Charlie wrote this series of letters on the board: A, C, E, G, I, K. If he continues the pattern, what should the next letter be?

   A J   C L

   B M   D N

4. Holly wrote this series of numbers: 2, 4, 6, 7, 8, 10, 12. What should the next number be if she continues the pattern?

   A 13   C 14

   B 15   D 16

Writing Math Karl did Problem 1 above and got a final answer of 10 inches. Was he correct? Explain.

_____

_____

_____

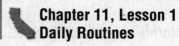
Hands On: Build Solids

Problem of the Day ———————————————— MR 2.4

Tina made the pattern below using 1-inch tiles.

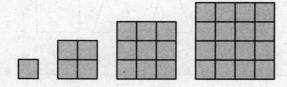

If she continues the pattern, what will be the area of the seventh figure?

Number Sense Review ——————————————— KEY

There are 28 students in Neil's third-grade class. Of those students, 11 take the bus to school, 8 arrive by car, and the others walk. How many students in Neil's class walk to school?

Word of the Day ——————————————————— KEY

rectangle

Count and write the number of rectangles you see during the day.

_____

_____

_____

Facts Practice ——————————————————— KEY NS 2.2

Multiply.

1. 7×2 2. 5×7 3. 7×8

4. 4×7 5. 6×7 6. 7×9

Hands On: Build Solids

CA Standards
MG 2.0, MG 2.5

Name the solid figures that have the faces shown.

1. □ □ □ □ □ □

_____

2. △ △ △ △ □

_____

3. ▭ ▭ ▭ ▭ ▭ ▭

_____

Write *true* or *false* for each. If false, write a statement that is true.

4. All faces of a square pyramid are squares.

_____

5. A rectangular prism and a cube have the same number of faces.

_____

Test Practice

Circle the letter of the correct answer.

6. Luann drew a solid figure. One of its faces is a triangle. Which solid did she draw?
   A cube   C square pyramid
   B cone   D rectangular prism

7. Tad painted a square pyramid. He painted each face a different color. How many colors did he use?
   A 4   C 5
   B 6   D 8

Writing Math A cube and a rectangular prism have the same number of faces, sides, and vertices. How are they different?

_____

_____

Solid Figures

Problem of the Day ——————————————— MG 2.5

Felicia is wrapping a box for a gift. The box has the shape of a rectangular prism. How many faces does the box have?

Geometry Review ——————————————— KEY MG 2.2

What triangle has three equal sides?

Number of the Day ——————————————— NS 1.1

6

Name 6 objects in your classroom that have 6 faces.

_____

_____

_____

Facts Practice ——————————————— KEY NS 2.1

Subtract mentally.

1. 85 − 5   2. 85 − 10   3. 85 − 15

4. 85 − 20   5. 85 − 25   6. 85 − 30

Solid Figures

CA Standards
MG 2.5, MG 2.6

Name the solid figures that make up the object.

1.

2.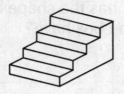

3.

4.

_____   _____   _____   _____

_____   _____   _____   _____

_____

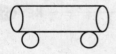 **Test Practice**

Circle the letter of the correct answer.

5. Marty drew the complex solid figure below. Which solids did he use?

   A 1 rectangular prism, 2 spheres

   B 1 sphere, 1 rectangular prism, 1 cone

   C 1 cylinder, 2 cones

   D 1 cylinder, 2 spheres

6. Duane wants to make a complex solid figure that will not roll off his desk. Which group of solids should he use?

   A cube, rectangular prism, square pyramid

   B sphere, cone, cylinder

   C cube, rectangular prism, sphere

   D cube, square pyramid, cylinder

 Writing Math Which solid figures can roll? Why?

_____

_____

Hands On: Explore Volume

Problem of the Day ———————————————— MG 2.5

Maruska has a tennis ball, a pair of number cubes, and a can of apple juice in her book bag. What three words could Maruska use to describe the geometric figures in her book bag?

Measurement Review ———————————— KEY MG 1.3

On Workmat 1, draw a square with a perimeter of 16 inches.

Number of the Day ———————————————— NS 1.1

941

What are some ways you can show 941?

_____

_____

_____

Facts Practice ———————————————— KEY NS 2.1

Add.

1. 882 + 164

2. 235 + 159

3. 177 + 197

4. 462 + 226

5. 370 + 318

Hands On: Explore Volume

CA Standards
KEY MG 1.2, MG 1.0

**Estimate the volume of the figure. Then build it with unit cubes.
Write the estimate and the number of unit cubes you used.**

1.

   Estimate: _____ unit cubes

   Exact: _____ unit cubes

2.

   Estimate: _____ unit cubes

   Exact: _____ unit cubes

3.

   Estimate: _____ unit cubes

   Exact: _____ unit cubes

4.

   Estimate: _____ unit cubes

   Exact: _____ unit cubes

5.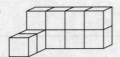

   Estimate: _____ unit cubes

   Exact: _____ unit cubes

6.

   Estimate: _____ unit cubes

   Exact: _____ unit cubes

Test Practice

Circle the letter of the correct answer.

7. How many cubes are in the figure
   below?

   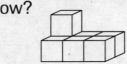

   A 6   C 7

   B 8   D 9

8. How many cubes are in the figure
   below?

   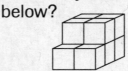

   A 6   C 8

   B 10   D 12

Writing Math Jack has 11 unit cubes. He wants to
use all of them to build a rectangular prism. Can he do this? Explain.

_____

_____

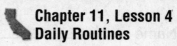

Find Volume

Problem of the Day
KEY MG 1.2

Jacob made a tower with 6 layers. Each layer was made of 2 unit cubes. What is the volume of Jacob's tower?

Measurement Review
KEY MG 1.3

Nathan is measuring a hexagon tile. Each side is 3 inches long. What is the perimeter of the tile?

Word of the Day
KEY MG 1.2

cubes

Estimate how many cubes you will need to fill your backpack. Fill your backpack with cubes. Record the number of cubes you used.

_____

_____

_____

Facts Practice
KEY NS 2.1

Subtract.

1. 800 − 348

2. 750 − 219

3. 765 − 185

4. 999 − 810

5. 822 − 307

Find Volume

Find the volume of the figure. Each = 1 cubic unit.

1.

2.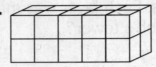

3.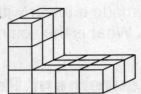

_____   _____   _____

Estimate the volume of the container in unit cubes.

4.

5.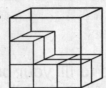

6.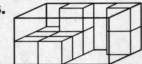

_____   _____   _____

Test Practice

Circle the letter of the correct answer.

7. What is the volume of the figure?

A 7 cubic units   **C** 8 cubic units

B 9 cubic units   **D** 12 cubic units

8. What is the volume of the figure?

A 9 cubic units   **C** 12 cubic units

B 18 cubic units   **D** 27 cubic units

 Writing Math Can you fill a container with an *odd* number of unit cubes? Explain.

_____

_____

_____

Problem Solving: Perimeter, Area, or Volume

Problem of the Day ——————————————————— KEY

A box has a volume of 24 unit cubes. It can hold three layers of cubes with the same number of cubes in each layer. How many unit cubes fit in each layer?

Number Sense Review ——————————————— KEY NS 1.3

Change the digit in the hundreds place of the number 3,807 to 5. Then add 2,817 to the new number. What is the sum?

Number of the Day ————————————————— KEY NS 2.2

20

Write multiplication sentences so that the product is 20.

_____

_____

_____

Facts Practice ——————————————————————— KEY

Estimate.

1. 16 + 10   2. 24 + 37   3. 56 + 91

4. 48 + 39   5. 82 + 29   6. 52 + 46

Name _____ Date _____

Problem Solving: Perimeter, Area, or Volume?

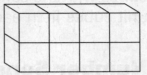

Solve each problem using perimeter, area or volume.

1. Marcy needs a fish tank that has at least 12 cubic units of space. Is the tank at the right big enough? Why or why not?

_____

_____

2. Larry is putting hardwood flooring down on the dance floor at the community youth center. He has enough flooring for 18 square units. Does he have enough for the job?

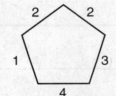

_____

_____

3. Selena is planning to make a border around the figure at the right. How many units of border will she need?

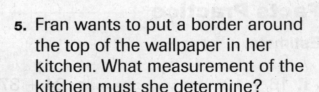

_____

Test Practice

Circle the letter of the correct answer.

4. Seth is choosing carpet to cover the floor of his den. What measurement of the room must he find before buying the carpeting?

   A the perimeter   C the area
   B the volume   D none of the above

5. Fran wants to put a border around the top of the wallpaper in her kitchen. What measurement of the kitchen must she determine?

   A the perimeter   C the area
   B the volume   D none of the above

 Writing Math Jolene multiplied the sides of the pentagon in Problem 3 to get the units needed. Was she correct? Explain.

_____

_____

Hands On: Model Division

Problem of the Day ———————————————— KEY MG 1.3

Jason wants to put a fence around a play area for his dog. How much fencing does he need if the entrance is 2 feet wide?

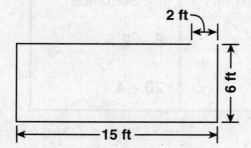

Number Sense Review ———————————————— KEY NS 2.2

In a third-grade classroom, there are 5 rows of desks. Each row has 7 desks. How many desks are in the classroom?

Number of the Day ———————————————— MR 2.3

11

Multiply 11 by factors from 1 to 9. What pattern do you observe in the products?

_____

_____

_____

Facts Practice ———————————————— KEY NS 2.2

Multiply.

1. 6×3 2. 3×7 3. 4×9

4. 3×6 5. 9×4 6. 7×3

Name _____ Date _____

Hands On: Model Division

CA Standards
NS 2.0, MR 2.3

Use counters to find the number in each equal group.
Then complete each division sentence.

	Number of Counters	Number of Equal Groups	Number in Each Group	Division Sentence
1.	8	2		8 ÷ 2 = _____
2.	20	4		20 ÷ 4 = _____

Use counters to find the number of equal groups.
Then complete each division sentence.

	Number of Counters	Number of Equal Groups	Number in Each Group	Division Sentence
3.	24		6	24 ÷ 6 = _____
4.	27		3	27 ÷ 3 = _____

Test Practice

Circle the letter of the correct answer.

5. Choose the division sentence that is modeled by the picture.

A 2 ÷ 2 = 1
B 6 ÷ 2 = 3
C 4 ÷ 2 = 2
D 4 ÷ 1 = 4

5. Which division sentence is modeled by the same figure?

8 × 3 = 24

A 8 ÷ 4 = 2
B 12 ÷ 3 = 4
C 15 ÷ 3 = 5
D 24 ÷ 8 = 3

Writing Math Describe two ways to divide 6 objects into equal groups.

Relate Division and Multiplication

Problem of the Day ———————————————————— NS 2.0

Luisa has 20 stamps. She wants to put an equal number of stamps on 5 sheets. How many stamps should go on each sheet?

Measurement Review ——————————————— KEY MG 1.3

The length of the side of an equilateral triangle is 7 centimeters. What is the perimeter in centimeters of the triangle?

Number of the Day ———————————————————— NS 1.1

1,234

Write 1,234 in word form.

_____

_____

_____

Facts Practice ———————————————————— KEY NS 2.2

Multiply.

1. 6×1 **2.** 2×4 **3.** 5×3

4. 7×2 **5.** 9×4 **6.** 10×3

Name _____ Date _____

Relate Multiplication and Division

CA Standards
KEY NS 2.3, MR 3.2

Use the array to complete the number sentence.

1.  _____ × 3 = 12

   _____ ÷ 4 = 3

2. 2 × _____ = 10

   10 ÷ _____ = 5

Draw an array for the multiplication sentence. Then write two related division sentences.

3. 3 × 2 = 6

_____

_____

4. 5 × 1 = 5

_____

_____

5. 2 × 6 = 12

_____

_____

Test Practice

Circle the letter of the correct answer.

6. Choose the multiplication and division sentences that the array shows.

   A 2 × 5 = 10
      10 ÷ 5 = 2

   B 3 × 4 = 12
      12 ÷ 3 = 4

   C 3 × 5 = 15
      15 ÷ 3 = 5

   D 3 × 6 = 18
      18 ÷ 3 = 6

7. Adrianne looked at an array and wrote this number sentence.

   36 ÷ 9 = 4

   Which number sentence could she complete to check her work?

   A 9 + 4 = ☐

   B 36 − 9 = ☐

   C 9 × 4 = ☐

   D 36 × 4 = ☐

Writing Math Is it always possible to write two division sentences for an array? Explain.

_____

_____

Different Ways to Divide

Problem of the Day ——————————————————— KEY NS 2.3

Draw an array for 2×5. Then write two related division sentences for the array.

Number Sense Review ——————————————————— KEY NS 2.3

The figure below is a model for the multiplication sentence.

9×2

Which division sentence is modeled by the same figure?

A $16 \div 2 = 8$

B $18 \div 9 = 2$

C $18 \div 3 = 6$

D $27 \div 9 = 3$

Word of the Day ——————————————————————— MR 2.3

array

Make an array to show the number of eggs in a carton.

_____

_____

_____

Facts Practice ——————————————————————— NS 2.0

Multiply or divide.

1. 5×4 2. $20 \div 5$ 3. 6×4

4. $24 \div 4$ 5. 8×4 6. $32 \div 8$

Name _____ Date _____

Different Ways to Divide

CA Standard
KEY NS 2.3

Use the picture to find the quotient.

1.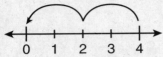

$4 \div 2 =$ _____

2.

$12 \div 2 =$ _____

3.

$8 \div 2 =$ _____

Use the multiplication fact to find the quotient.

4. $3 \times 2 = 6$

$6 \div 2$ _____

5. $7 \times 2 = 14$

$14 \div 2$ _____

6. $5 \times 2 = 10$

$10 \div 2$ _____

7. $9 \times 2 = 18$

$18 \div 2$ _____

8. $10 \times 2 = 20$

$20 \div 2$ _____

9. $8 \times 2 = 16$

$16 \div 2$ _____

10. $1 \times 2 = 2$

$2 \div 2$ _____

11. $4 \times 2 = 8$

$8 \div 2$ _____

Find the quotient. Tell which way you used.

12. $18 \div 2$ _____

13. $8 \div 2$ _____

14. $10 \div 2$ _____

15. $20 \div 2$ _____

Test Practice

Circle the letter of the correct answer.

16. Choose the division sentence that the number line shows.

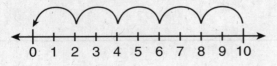

A $8 \div 2 = 4$ c $10 \div 2 = 5$

B $12 \div 2 = 6$ D $14 \div 2 = 7$

17. Ice-cream cones cost $2 each. If Linda has $12, how many ice-cream cones can she buy?

A 2 c 6

B 4 D 10

Writing Math Avram counted back 6 times from 42 to solve a division problem. What was the problem? Explain.

Practice Dividing by 2, 5, or 10

Problem of the Day ———————————————————— NS 2.5

Find 20 ÷ 4. Tell which strategy you used and why.

Number Sense Review ——————————————— KEY **NS 1.3**

Garret's address is 4713 Franklin Street. Which digit is in the thousands place?

Word of the Day ——————————————————— NS 2.0

division

Write a division problem. Show four ways how to solve it.

_____

_____

_____

Facts Practice ——————————————————————— NS 2.0

Find the quotient.

1. 8 ÷ 2   **2.** 20 ÷ 4   **3.** 45 ÷ 9

4. 16 ÷ 4   **5.** 40 ÷ 8   **6.** 32 ÷ 4

Name _____ Date _____

Practice Dividing by 2, 5, or 10

CA Standards
KEY NS 2.3, MR 2.0

Use the array to help you find the quotient.

1.

    30 ÷ 5 = _____

2.

    45 ÷ 5 = _____

3. 25 ÷ 5 = _____

Divide. Check by multiplying.

4. $5\overline{)50}$ 5. $5\overline{)25}$ 6. $2\overline{)14}$ 7. $5\overline{)35}$ 8. $10\overline{)20}$

9. 15 ÷ 5 =   10. 16 ÷ 2 =   11. 40 ÷ 10 =   12. 35 ÷ 5 =   13. 20 ÷ 2 =

_____   _____   _____   _____   _____

Test Practice

Circle the letter of the correct answer.

14. Choose the quotient.

    45 ÷ 5 =

    A 7   C 8

    B 9   D 10

15. Heather has 20 pennies. She divides her pennies into 10 equal piles. How many pennies are in each pile?

    A 2   C 5

    B 4   D 10

Writing Math Mina says that if you know the products up to 10 × 10, you also know the division facts up to a dividend of 100. Is she right? Explain.

_____

_____

_____

Problem Solving: Field Trip

Problem of the Day ———————————————— NS 2.5

Erica has 30 plums. How many baskets can she make if she puts 5 plums in each basket? How many baskets can she make if she puts 10 plums in each basket?

Algebra Review ———————————————— KEY **AF 1.1**

Bryant has 3 dogs. He takes each dog for a walk 4 times a day. Write a number sentence to find the total number of walks Bryant does with his dogs each day.

Number of the Day ———————————————— KEY **NS 1.5**

10,538,005

Write 10,538,005 using expanded notation.

_____

_____

_____

Facts Practice ———————————————— AF 1.4

Find the number of inches.

1. 2 feet

2. 5 feet

3. 10 feet

4. 12 feet

Hands On: Use a Multiplication Table to Divide

Problem of the Day ———————————————————————— NS 2.5

Mrs. Wolf has a box of 45 crayons. She wants to give each of 5 students the same number of crayons. How many crayons should she give to each student?

Number Sense Review ———————————————————— KEY NS 2.1

Jake has 586 points in a video game. What is 125 more than 586?

Number of the Day ————————————————————————— KEY NS 2.2

16

What numbers can you multiply to get 16?

_____

_____

_____

Facts Practice ———————————————————————————— NS 2.0

Divide.

1. 8 ÷ 2   2. 30 ÷ 5   3. 50 ÷ 10

4. 2)‾1‾8‾   5. 5)‾4‾5‾   6. 10)‾6‾0‾

Hands On: Use a Multiplication Table to Divide

CA Standard
KEY NS 2.3

Use the multiplication table to help you do the problems.

×	0	1	2	3	4	5	6	7	8	9	10
0	0	0	0	0	0	0	0	0	0	0	0
1	0	1	2	3	4	5	6	7	8	9	10
2	0	2	4	6	8	10	12	14	16	18	20
3	0	3	6	9	12	15	18	21	24	27	30
4	0	4	8	12	16	20	24	28	32	36	40
5	0	5	10	15	20	25	30	35	40	45	50
6	0	6	12	18	24	30	36	42	48	54	60
7	0	7	14	21	28	35	42	49	56	63	70
8	0	8	16	24	32	40	48	56	64	72	80
9	0	9	18	27	36	45	54	63	72	81	90
10	0	10	20	30	40	50	60	70	80	90	100

Divide.

1. $6\overline{)42}$ 2. $7\overline{)49}$ 3. $6\overline{)54}$ 4. $10\overline{)70}$

5. $80 \div 8 =$ _____   6. $21 \div 7 =$ _____

7. $8 \div 8 =$ _____   8. $72 \div 8 =$ _____

Test Practice

Circle the letter of the correct answer.

9. Doug bought 48 baseball cards. The cards came in packs of 8. How many packs of baseball cards did Doug buy?

A 6   C 8
B 10   D 18

10. Kati divided 28 coins into 7 equal stacks. How many coins were in each stack?

A 3   C 4
B 5   D 6

Writing Math Use a multiplication table to help solve a division problem. In what order do you find the quotient, the divisor, and the dividend?

_____

_____

Practice Dividing by 3 or 4

Problem of the Day

Emily drew 49 designs. She had them divided equally on 7 pages
of her notebook. Use a multiplication table to find how many
designs were on each page.

Measurement Review

Garrett made the following design.

Each ☐ = 1 square unit.

What is the area of Garrett's design?

Number of the Day

0

When you multiply my number by any number, the product is 0.
When you add my number to any number, the sum is the other
number. What's my number?

Facts Practice

Subtract.

1. $12 - 5$ 2. $10 - 3$ 3. $14 - 7$

4. $8 - 4$ 5. $15 - 5$ 6. $12 - 6$

Name _____ Date _____

Practice Dividing by 3 or 4

CA Standards
KEY NS 2.3, NS 2.0

Find the quotient.

1. 3)9 2. 4)12 3. 3)12 4. 4)20 5. 3)3

6. 3)15 7. 4)8 8. 3)0 9. 3)18 10. 3)27

11. 21 ÷ 3 _____ 12. 28 ÷ 4 _____ 13. 30 ÷ 3 _____ 14. 24 ÷ 3 _____

15. 18 ÷ 3 _____ 16. 0 ÷ 3 _____ 17. 16 ÷ 4 _____ 18. 3 ÷ 3 _____

Write <, >, or = in the ◯.

19. 3 × 2 ◯ 12 ÷ 2 20. 9 × 3 ◯ 9 + 3 21. 30 ÷ 3 ◯ 30 − 3

22. 3 × 3 ◯ 18 ÷ 2 23. 17 − 9 ◯ 5 × 2 24. 21 ÷ 3 ◯ 6 × 3

25. 3 − 3 ◯ 3 ÷ 1 26. 7 + 9 ◯ 10 − 7 27. 3 + 3 ◯ 2 × 3

Test Practice

28. Choose the division sentence that the number line shows.

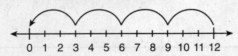

   0 1 2 3 4 5 6 7 8 9 10 11 12

   A 0 ÷ 3 = 0   **C** 3 ÷ 3 = 1

   B 12 ÷ 3 = 4   **D** 9 ÷ 3 = 3

29. Emily baked 16 muffins. She divided them equally between 4 tables. How many muffins were on each table?

   A 4   **C** 6

   B 6   **D** 7

Writing Math Eva wanted to find the quotient of 32 ÷ 4. She started at 32 on the number line and counted backwards by 4. How does this give her the correct answer of 8?

_____

_____

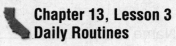
Fact Families

Problem of the Day ———————————————————————— NS 2.5

Each book at the book fair costs $3.00. Monica spent $12.00 on books. How many books did Monica buy?

Number Sense Review ———————————————————— KEY NS 2.1

If 63 more than a number is 283, what is the number?

Number of the Day ———————————————————————— NS 2.0

24

What are some ways you can make 24?

_____

_____

_____

Facts Practice ———————————————————————————— NS 2.0

Find each product or quotient.

1. 4×6 2. $24 \div 6$ 3. $24 \div 4$

4. 8×4 5. $32 \div 8$ 6. $32 \div 4$

Fact Families

CA Standards
KEY NS 2.3, AF 1.2

Complete the fact family.

1. $1 \times 6 = 6$

$6 \times \underline{\hspace{1cm}} = 6$

$6 \div 1 = \underline{\hspace{1cm}}$

$6 \div \underline{\hspace{1cm}} = 1$

2. $4 \times 7 = 28$

$\underline{\hspace{1cm}} \times 4 = 28$

$28 \div \underline{\hspace{1cm}} = 7$

$28 \div \underline{\hspace{1cm}} = 4$

3. $8 \times 5 = 40$

$5 \times \underline{\hspace{1cm}} = 40$

$40 \div 5 = \underline{\hspace{1cm}}$

$\underline{\hspace{1cm}} \div 8 = 5$

4. $3 \times 9 = 27$

$9 \times 3 = \underline{\hspace{1cm}}$

$\underline{\hspace{1cm}} \div 3 = 9$

$27 \div 9 = \underline{\hspace{1cm}}$

Write a fact family for the set of numbers.

5. 2, 4, 8

6. 10, 6, 60

7. 5, 3, 15

8. 5, 5, 25

_____ _____ _____ _____

_____ _____ _____ _____

_____ _____ _____ _____

_____ _____ _____ _____

Test Practice

Circle the letter of the correct answer.

9. Choose the fact that belongs to the same fact family as $4 \times 2 = 8$.

A $2 \times 2 = 4$ B $4 \div 2 = 2$

C $8 \div 2 = 4$ D $1 \times 8 = 8$

10. Choose the fact that belongs to the same fact family as $2 \times 5 = 10$.

A $10 \div 5 = 2$ B $2 + 5 = 7$

C $5 \times 10 = 2$ D $10 \div 5 = 5$

Writing Math Why do some fact families have only two facts? Give an example.

Practice Dividing by 9

Problem of the Day

Terrence knows $2 \times 10 = 20$. Write a fact that belongs to the same fact family.

Geometry Review

Danielle drew a quadrilateral. It has 4 equal sides and 4 right angles. What quadrilateral did Danielle draw?

Word of the Day

related fact

Write three related facts to $8 \times 5 = 40$.

_____

_____

_____

Facts Practice

Multiply.

1. 4×9 2. 9×3 3. 8×9

4. 9×6 5. 7×9 6. 9×9

Practice Dividing by 9

CA Standards
KEY NS 2.3, AF 1.2

Find the factor and quotient.

1. $9 \times$ _____ $= 18$ 2. $9 \times$ _____ $= 45$ 3. $9 \times$ _____ $= 63$

$18 \div 9 =$ _____ $45 \div 9 =$ _____ $63 \div 9 =$ _____

Divide.

4. $9\overline{)0}$ 5. $9\overline{)90}$ 6. $9\overline{)54}$ 7. $9\overline{)45}$ 8. $9\overline{)72}$

Find the rule. Then complete the table.

9.

Rule: _____	
36	4
54	6
18	2
10.	7
11. 0	

12.

Rule: _____	
25	5
35	7
10	2
13. 45	
14.	4

15.

Rule: _____	
42	7
30	5
18	3
16.	9
17. 48	

Test Practice

Circle the letter of the correct answer.

18. Susan has 63 books to display in a bookcase. If she puts 9 books on each shelf, how many shelves will she fill?

A 6   C 7

B 8   D 9

19. Which division fact is related to the multiplication fact?

$$8 \times 5 = 40$$

A $80 \div 10 = 8$ C $32 \div 8 = 4$

B $35 \div 7 = 5$ D $40 \div 8 = 5$

Writing Math Would you use equal groups, a related multiplication fact, or a related division fact to find the quotient of $54 \div 9$? Explain.

Problem Solving: Equal Groups Problems

Problem of the Day ————————————————————————— NS 2.5

The 27 students in Ms. Diaz's class are forming equal groups. Each group will study one of 9 different jobs that people do. How many students are in each group?

Number Sense Review ——————————————————— KEY NS 2.1

Philip rode his bicycle 2 miles each day for 7 days. What is the total number of miles he rode his bicycle? If Philip continues the pattern, how many miles will he ride in 14 days?

Number of the Day ————————————————————— KEY NS 2.2

6

Name all the multiples of 6 that are less than 75.

_____

_____

_____

Facts Practice ——————————————————————————— KEY NS 2.2

Find each factor or product.

1. $7 \times 8 =$ ▢

2. $6 \times$ ▢ $= 42$

3. ▢ $\times 7 = 70$

4. $9 \times 5 =$ ▢

Problem Solving: Equal Groups Problems

CA Standards
KEY NS 2.3, MR 2.4

Solve each problem involving equal groups.

1. A group of students and their chaperones hiked for 5 hours. They hiked 3 miles per hour. How many miles did they hike in all?

_____

2. The campers set up camp for the night. They set up 7 tents. There were 28 students and their chaperones. How many people were assigned to each tent for the night?

_____

3. In the morning, the students and their chaperones had pancakes for breakfast. They ate a total of 112 pancakes. If they all ate the same number, how many pancakes did each person eat?

_____

Test Practice

4. Sarah spends 2 hours doing her homework each night, Monday through Friday. How many hours of homework does she do in a week?

   A 10 hours   c 12 hours

   B 8 hours   D 6 hours

5. There are 36 students in Mr. Martin's class. There are 6 equal rows of desks. How many students sit in each row?

   A 3 students   c 4 students

   B 6 students   D 8 students

Writing Math What necessary piece of information is missing from problem 3 above? Where did you find it?

_____

_____

Hands On: Division Rules

Problem of the Day ———————————————————————— NS 2.5

Ella wants to share 18 counters by dividing them into equal
groups. She puts more than one counter in each group. What is
the greatest number of equal groups Ella can make if she uses
all the counters?

Number Sense Review ———————————————————————— NS 2.0

The array below is a model for a multiplication sentence.

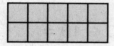

What multiplication sentence is modeled by this array?

Number of the Day ———————————————————————— NS 1.1

101

This number reads the same forward and backward. How many
other three-digit numbers can you think of that read the same
forward and backward?

_____

_____

_____

Facts Practice ———————————————————————— NS 2.6

Multiply.

1. 1×8

2. 4×1

3. 0×3

4. 6×0

5. 1×5

6. 0×2

Hands On: Division Rules

CA Standards
NS 2.6, MR 3.0

Divide.

1. $5\overline{)25}$ 2. $8\overline{)0}$ 3. $2\overline{)8}$ 4. $1\overline{)0}$ 5. $1\overline{)10}$

6. $8\overline{)8}$ 7. $10\overline{)40}$ 8. $5\overline{)40}$ 9. $6\overline{)6}$ 10. $9\overline{)0}$

11. $1\overline{)4}$ 12. $2\overline{)12}$ 13. $10\overline{)80}$ 14. $1\overline{)3}$ 15. $2\overline{)16}$

16. $8 \div 1 =$ 17. $10 \div 10 =$ 18. $35 \div 5 =$ 19. $90 \div 10 =$

_____ _____ _____ _____

20. $0 \div 10 =$ 21. $10 \div 2 =$ 22. $7 \div 7 =$ 23. $9 \div 1 =$

_____ _____ _____ _____

Test Practice

Circle the letter of the correct answer.

24. Choose the division sentence that can be solved using this division rule: When any number is divided by 1, the quotient is that number.

A $486 \div 1 = n$ C $486 \div 486 = n$

B $0 \div 486 = n$ D $486 \div 2Đ = n$

25. What is the quotient for 0 divided by 2?

A 0 C 2

B 1 D 20

Writing Math Write three division sentences that can be solved using this division rule: When any number except 0 is divided by itself, the quotient is 1.

_____

_____

Practice Dividing by 6

Problem of the Day —————————————— NS 2.6

Janet walks the same distance every day. She walks 7 miles every week. How many miles does she walk each day?

Number Sense Review —————————————— NS 1.1

1. Write 378 in word form.

2. Write five hundred twenty-three in standard form.

Number of the Day —————————————— KEY NS 2.1

945

If you add the last two digits, $4 + 5$, they equal 9, the first digit. Write as many three-digit numbers as you can in which the sum of the last two digits equals 9, the first digit.

_____

_____

_____

Facts Practice —————————————— KEY NS 2.2

Multiply.

1. 6×5 2. 3×6 3. 6×8

4. 10×6 5. 9×6 6. 6×2

Practice Dividing by 6

CA Standards
KEY NS 2.3, MR 2.4

Find the quotient.

1. $6\overline{)18}$ 2. $6\overline{)24}$ 3. $6\overline{)6}$ 4. $6\overline{)36}$ 5. $6\overline{)30}$

6. $6\overline{)12}$ 7. $6\overline{)60}$ 8. $6\overline{)0}$ 9. $6\overline{)48}$ 10. $6\overline{)42}$

11. $30 \div 6 =$ _____ 12. $48 \div 6 =$ _____ 13. $18 \div 6 =$ _____

14. $6 \div 6 =$ _____ 15. $54 \div 6 =$ _____ 16. $36 \div 6 =$ _____

17. $60 \div 6 =$ _____ 18. $42 \div 6 =$ _____ 19. $24 \div 6 =$ _____

Write <, >, or = in each ◯.

20. $48 \div 6$ ◯ 9 21. $54 \div 6$ ◯ 8 22. $24 \div 3$ ◯ $42 \div 6$

Test Practice

Circle the letter of the correct answer.

23. Janet has 54 stickers in her album. Each page in the album has 6 stickers. How many pages are in Janet's sticker album?

   A 6   C 9

   B 8   D 10

24. Marco is putting 24 cupcakes into boxes. Each box can hold 6 cupcakes. How many boxes does he need?

   A 3   C 5

   B 4   D 6

 Writing Math Ms. Barton is making teams of 6 students for a math competition. If there are 22 students in the class, how many complete teams will she be able to make? Will all students be placed on a team? Explain.

_____

_____

Practice Dividing by 7

Problem of the Day ———————————————————— NS 2.5

Shondra wants to put 24 plants in the rows of her garden. She wants to put the same number of plants in 6 rows. How many plants are in each row?

Geometry Review ———————————————————— KEY MG 1.3

What is the perimeter of a rectangle with length 8 inches and width 4 inches?

Word of the Day ———————————————————— NS 2.0

divide

Have students use Workmat 1 to draw a picture that illustrates something being divided. Then ask students to write a sentence using the word divide.

_____

_____

_____

Facts Practice ———————————————————— KEY NS 2.2

Multiply.

1. 7×2

2. 5×7

3. 7×9

4. 7×4

5. 6×7

6. 10×7

Practice Dividing by 7

CA Standard
KEY NS 2.3

Divide.

1. $7\overline{)35}$ 2. $7\overline{)49}$ 3. $7\overline{)14}$ 4. $7\overline{)70}$ 5. $7\overline{)0}$

6. $7\overline{)21}$ 7. $7\overline{)63}$ 8. $7\overline{)7}$ 9. $7\overline{)42}$ 10. $7\overline{)56}$

11. $28 \div 7 =$ _____   12. $14 \div 7 =$ _____   13. $63 \div 7 =$ _____

14. $7 \div 7 =$ _____   15. $56 \div 7 =$ _____   16. $49 \div 7 =$ _____

 **Test Practice**

Circle the letter of the correct answer.

17. The party store ordered 35 balloons in 7 different colors. If the same number of each color is ordered, how many of each color is ordered?

   A 4   c 6

   B 5   D 7

18. Jesse has 63 stamps arranged in rows with 7 stamps in each row. How many rows of stamps does Jesse have?

   A 7   c 9

   B 8   D 10

 Writing Math How could knowing that $35 \div 7 = 5$ help you find $42 \div 7$? Explain.

_____

_____

Practice Dividing by 8

Problem of the Day
KEY NS 2.3

Nola is half the age of Susan. Brian is twice the age of Susan. Susan is 14 years old. How old is Nola? How old is Brian?

Patterns Review
KEY NS 1.3

Use Workmat 3 to help you write the place value of the underlined digit.

1. 2,1<u>57</u>

2. 5,<u>8</u>36

3. <u>3</u>,079

4. 2,41<u>3</u>

Number of the Day
KEY NS 1.5

763

Write the number in word form and expanded form.

_____

_____

Facts Practice
KEY NS 2.2

Multiply.

1. 8×2 2. 5×8 3. 4×8

4. 8×7 5. 3×8 6. 8×9

Practice Dividing by 8

Divide.

1. $8\overline{)40}$ 2. $8\overline{)56}$ 3. $8\overline{)16}$ 4. $8\overline{)72}$ 5. $8\overline{)8}$

6. $8\overline{)24}$ 7. $8\overline{)0}$ 8. $8\overline{)32}$ 9. $8\overline{)48}$ 10. $8\overline{)64}$

11. $16 \div 8 =$ _____   12. $80 \div 8 =$ _____   13. $72 \div 8 =$ _____

14. $8 \div 8 =$ _____   15. $64 \div 8 =$ _____   16. $0 \div 8 =$ _____

Find each missing number.

17. $b \times 8 = 56$ 18. $8 \div 8 = p$ 19. $40 \div 8 = a$

$b =$ _____ $p =$ _____ $a =$ _____

Test Practice

Circle the letter of the correct answer.

20. Each table in a restaurant seats 8 people. How many tables are needed to seat a party of 64 people?

A 6   c 8

B 7   D 9

21. James invited 24 people to a birthday party. If one cake is enough for 8 guests, how many cakes does James need to buy?

A 2   c 4

B 3   D 5

 Writing Math Why is $40 \div 8$ less than $48 \div 8$?

_____

_____

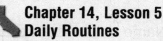
Problem Solving: Work Backward

Problem of the Day ———————————————————— NS 2.5

Cathy puts 48 raisins into groups to go on top of muffins. She wants each muffin to have the same number of raisins. Cathy is making 8 muffins. How many raisins go in each group?

Number Sense Review ———————————————— NS 1.2

Write each set of numbers in order from least to greatest. Use Workmat 3 to help you.

1. 787; 803; 759

2. 5,943; 6,103; 6,098

Number of the Day ———————————————— KEY NS 2.1

312

The sum of the digits of the number is 6. Write as many three-digit numbers as you can think of whose digits add up to 6.

_____

_____

_____

Facts Practice ———————————————————— KEY NS 2.1

Add or subtract.

1. $463 + 87$

2. $92 - 54$

3. $893 + 421$

4. $607 - 429$

Problem Solving: Work Backward

Work backward to solve each problem.

1. Jerry took his younger sister and her friend to the movies. The cost for 1 adult ticket and 2 children's tickets was $18. If Jerry's ticket cost $8, how much did each child's ticket cost?

_____

2. Irina bought 9 Valentine's Day cards for her friends and a box of chocolates for her mother. She spent a total of $32. If the box of chocolates cost her $14, how much did she spend for each Valentine's card?

_____

3. Wally cut a board into 5 equal pieces. Then he cut 2 inches off one of the pieces. The piece that was left was 7 inches long. How long was the original board?

_____

Test Practice

Circle the letter of the correct answer.

4. Dan's class has 3 rows of girls and 3 rows of boys. The rows of girls total 12 girls. How many girls are in each equal row?

   A 4   C 2

   B 3   D 6

5. If the total number of students in Dan's class is 27, and the number of boys in each row is the same, how many boys are in each row?

   A 3   C 4

   B 6   D 5

Writing Math When Lynn did problem 3 above, she subtracted 2 from 7 inches to get 5 inches. Will she get the correct answer? Explain.

_____

_____

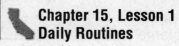
Hands On: Model Fractions

Problem of the Day ──────────────────────── MR 2.0

Work backward to solve the problem.

Leon weighed a bag of pears. Then he added 4 pounds of pears
to the bag. After he took out 5 pounds of pears, the bag weighed
3 pounds. How much did the bag weigh at the start?

Number Sense Review ──────────────────────── NS 2.0

Write the multiplication and division sentences in the fact
family for 6, 7, and 42.

Number of the Day ──────────────────────── NS 1.1

432

What are different ways you can represent 432?

_____

_____

_____

Facts Practice ──────────────────────── NS 1.4

Round each number to the greatest place.

1. 152

2. 74

3. 918

4. 547

5. 673

Name _____ Date _____

Model Fractions

CA Standard
NS 3.0

Write the fraction for the part that is shaded.

1.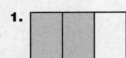

2.

3.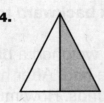

4.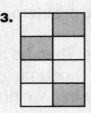

_____   _____   _____

Draw a picture to show the fraction.

5. $\frac{3}{4}$ 6. $\frac{8}{10}$ 7. $\frac{4}{7}$

Test Practice

Circle the letter of the correct answer.

8. Which figure has $\frac{3}{4}$ shaded?

A   C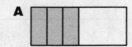

B   D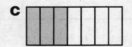

9. Which is an improper fraction?

A $\frac{1}{3}$ C $\frac{2}{3}$

B $\frac{3}{4}$ D $\frac{4}{3}$

Writing Math The fractions $\frac{3}{4}$ and $\frac{4}{3}$ use the same numbers. Tell why they describe different amounts.

_____

_____

Fractions and Groups

Problem of the Day ———————————————— NS 3.0

Seven students each ate $\frac{1}{4}$ of a pizza. Did they eat more or less than a whole pizza? Explain your answer.

Algebra Review ———————————————— AF 2.2

Draw a picture to show the pattern.

There are 18 cars parked in a row. Every sixth car is red. How many red cars are there in all?

Number of the Day ———————————————— MR 1.1

100

Why is the number 100 important?

_____

_____

_____

Facts Practice ———————————————— KEY NS 2.1

Find each sum.

1. $256 + 73$

2. $472 + 314$

3. $165 + 790$

4. $348 + 226$

5. $659 + 186$

Fractions and Groups

Write a fraction to name the part of the group that is shaded.

1.   _____

2.   _____

3.   _____

4.   _____

Use the picture on the right to answer questions 5 and 6.

5. What fraction of the triangles are striped?

   _____

6. Which kind of triangles—the white, the shaded, or striped—are $\frac{1}{8}$ of the group?

   _____

Test Practice

Circle the letter of the correct answer.

7. Marcus has 10 beads. He painted 4 of the beads blue. He painted 6 of the beads yellow. What fraction of the beads did Marcus paint yellow?

   A $\frac{4}{6}$ C $\frac{4}{10}$

   B $\frac{6}{10}$ D $\frac{6}{4}$

8. Lorraine has 5 balloons. One of the balloons is red. What fraction of the ballons are **not** red?

   A $\frac{1}{5}$ C $\frac{2}{5}$

   B $\frac{3}{5}$ D $\frac{4}{5}$

  Writing Math There are 6 kittens. Can the fraction $\frac{0}{6}$ describe a part of this group? Explain why or why not.

_____

_____

Hands On: Model Equivalent Fractions

Problem of the Day ———————————————— NS 3.0

The pet store has 9 animals for sale. They have 2 cats and 3 birds. The rest are dogs. What fraction of the animals are dogs?

Number Sense Review ———————————————— NS 2.0

Write a number sentence you could use to solve the problem.

Tanisha used 348 beads to make a belt. She has 126 beads left. How many beads did she have when she started?

Number of the Day ———————————————— KEY

9

Write out the multiples of 9 from 9 to 90. Add the digits of each multiple. What do you get?

_____

_____

_____

Facts Practice ———————————————— Grade 2 KEY NS 3.2

Find the quotient and remainder.

1. $19 \div 8$

2. $27 \div 6$

3. $30 \div 9$

4. $22 \div 3$

5. $23 \div 7$

Model Equivalent Fractions

CA Standards
NS 3.1, MR 1.1

Write *equivalent* or *not equivalent* to describe the fractions in the pair.

1.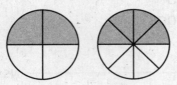

_____

2.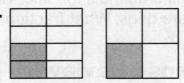

_____

3.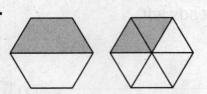

_____

4.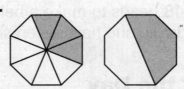

_____

Use the circles to complete the equivalent fractions.

5.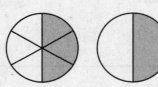

$$\frac{3}{6} = \frac{\square}{2} \underline{\quad}$$

6.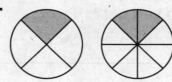

$$\frac{1}{4} = \frac{\square}{8} \underline{\quad}$$

Test Practice

Circle the letter of the correct answer.

7. Jeanne has 10 flowers. Four are red. Which numerator would she use to show the fraction of red flowers?

A 4   C 6

B 10   D 14

8. Matthew has 10 flowers. Four are red. Which numerator would he use to show the fraction of flowers that are not red?

A 4   C 10

B 6   D 14

 Writing Math Are $\frac{3}{4}$ and $\frac{4}{5}$ equivalent fractions? How do you know? Explain.

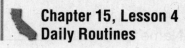
Find Equivalent Fractions

Problem of the Day ——————————————————————— NS 3.1

Tia divided her poster into 4 equal parts. Ben divided his poster into 8 equal parts. They both colored $\frac{3}{4}$ of their posters red. How many parts of their posters did Tia and Ben color red?

Measurement Review ——————————————————————— MG 1.1

Name three objects that are close to 6 inches long.

Number of the Day ——————————————————————— KEY NS 2.1

231

Add the digits. The sum is 6. Write four other 3-digit numbers whose digits add to 6.

_____

_____

_____

Facts Practice ——————————————————————— KEY NS 2.1

Subtract.

1. 94 − 76

2. 85 − 23

3. 500 − 47

4. 628 − 161

5. 900 − 259

Find Equivalent Fractions

Write *equivalent* or *not equivalent* to describe the fractions.

1.

2.

_____ _____

Name the equivalent fractions shown.

3.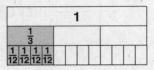

$$\frac{\square}{3} = \frac{\square}{12}$$

_____

4.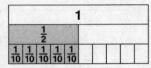

$$\frac{\square}{2} = \frac{\square}{10}$$

_____

5.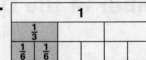

$$\frac{\square}{3} = \frac{\square}{6}$$

_____

Test Practice

Circle the letter of the correct answer.

6. Lois had 12 eggs. She used 4 eggs to bake a cake. Which shows an equivalent fraction for the part of the eggs Lois used?

   A $\frac{3}{6}$ C $\frac{1}{3}$

   B $\frac{3}{12}$ D $\frac{6}{12}$

7. Angie folded a circle into 8 equal parts. She colored all but 6 parts red. Which fraction is not equivalent to the part of the circle that is red?

   A $\frac{1}{4}$ C $\frac{3}{12}$

   B $\frac{6}{8}$ D $\frac{2}{8}$

 Writing Math Are $\frac{2}{6}$, $\frac{1}{3}$, and $\frac{4}{12}$ equivalent fractions? How do you know?

_____

Hands On: Compare Fractions

Problem of the Day —————————————————————— NS 3.1

Ty and Amir each made a pizza. Ty cut his pizza into 8 equal slices. Amir cut his pizza into 6 equal slices. Each ate half of his own pizza. How many slices of pizza did each boy eat?

Number Sense Review ————————————————————— NS 1.2

Use the digits 3, 5, and 8 to make four numbers less than 600.

Word of the Day ——————————————————————— NS 1.2

compare

Give some examples of when you might compare during the school day.

_____

_____

Facts Practice —————————————————————— KEY NS 2.2

Multiply.

1. 7×9

2. 8×6

3. 10×5

4. 6×4

5. 9×9

Compare Fractions

CA Standard
NS 3.1

Compare the fractions. Write < or > for the ☐. Use fraction tiles or number lines to help you.

1.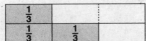

$\dfrac{1}{3}$ ☐ $\dfrac{2}{3}$

2.

$\dfrac{1}{5}$ ☐ $\dfrac{1}{2}$

3.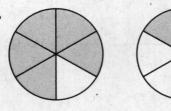

$\dfrac{5}{6}$ ☐ $\dfrac{2}{6}$

4.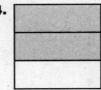

$\dfrac{2}{3}$ ☐ $\dfrac{3}{4}$

5. $\dfrac{1}{3}$ ☐ $\dfrac{1}{6}$

6. $\dfrac{3}{4}$ ☐ $\dfrac{1}{4}$

7. $\dfrac{5}{6}$ ☐ $\dfrac{3}{6}$

 Test Practice

Circle the letter of the correct answer.

8. Nina has a quilt. $\dfrac{1}{3}$ of the squares on it are pink. Rosa has the same size quilt. The fraction of pink squares on her quilt is greater. Which fraction shows the pink squares on Rosa's quilt?

A $\dfrac{1}{2}$ C $\dfrac{1}{4}$

B $\dfrac{1}{5}$ D $\dfrac{1}{6}$

9. Tyrone and Jerome have the same number of marbles. $\dfrac{3}{6}$ of Tyrone's marbles are blue. Jerome has fewer blue marbles. Which fraction shows the number of blue marbles Jerome has?

A $\dfrac{1}{2}$ C $\dfrac{1}{6}$

B $\dfrac{2}{4}$ D $\dfrac{4}{6}$

Writing Math Kate ate $\dfrac{3}{3}$ of a sandwich. Cao ate $\dfrac{7}{7}$ of a sandwich that was the same size as Kate's. Who ate more? Explain your answer.

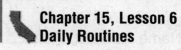

Problem Solving: Too Much Information

Problem of the Day ———————————————— NS 3.1

Shane and Latoya shared a sandwich. Shane ate $\frac{1}{3}$ of the sandwich. Latoya ate $\frac{5}{8}$ of the sandwich. Who ate more?

Geometry Review ——————————————————— MG 2.4

Name three different times at which the hands of a clock make a right angle.

Number of the Day ————————————————— NS 1.1

500

What are different ways you can represent 500?

_____

_____

_____

Facts Practice ——————————————————— NS 2.5

Divide.

1. $27 \div 3$

2. $16 \div 8$

3. $81 \div 9$

4. $24 \div 4$

5. $49 \div 7$

Too Much Information

Solve. Tell what information is not needed to solve the problem.

1. A parking lot near the sports field holds a total of 52 vehicles. There are 42 cars parked there now. Half of these cars are red, 10 are blue, and the rest are silver. What fraction of the cars are silver?

   _____

2. Two-thirds of the musicians in a 16-piece band are girls. The 16 musicians include 12 brass players. What fraction of the band plays brass instruments?

   _____

3. A pile of index cards has a mixture of white, pink, yellow, red, and blue cards. Some cards are lined, and some are unlined. The total number of cards is 150. $\frac{2}{5}$ of the cards are blue, 10 cards are white, and 10 cards are red. Half of the remaining cards are pink. How many cards are yellow?

   _____

4. Justin took photographs during a trip to the mountains. He used one roll of color film and one roll of black-and-white film. He took $\frac{1}{3}$ of the pictures in color during a picnic with his family. If he took 36 pictures in all, how many color pictures did he take during the picnic?

   _____

Test Practice

Circle the letter of the correct answer.

5. Rogelio has 3 one-dollar bills, 5 quarters, 4 dimes, 2 nickels, and 9 pennies. What fraction of the coins are quarters?

   A $\frac{1}{2}$ **C** $\frac{1}{4}$

   B $\frac{1}{5}$ **D** $\frac{4}{10}$

6. Eveline has 18 classmates. $\frac{2}{3}$ of these students are boys. Half of her classmates live on her street. How many of Eveline's classmates are girls?

   A 6   **C** 12

   B 9   **D** 16

Hands On: Add and Subtract Fractions

Problem of the Day ———————————————— MR 1.1

What information is not needed to solve this problem?

Concert tickets cost $8 for adults and $5 for children. You buy 6 adult tickets and 10 children's tickets. How many tickets do you buy?

Number Sense Review ———————————————— NS 2.0

Draw a picture to show 12 fish placed equally in 3 aquariums. Write a number sentence that tells how many fish are in each aquarium.

Number of the Day ———————————————— MR 1.1

28

Make up a problem about weeks and days that has 28 as the answer.

_____

_____

Facts Practice ———————————————— NS 1.4

Round each number to the nearest ten.

1. 842

2. 6,291

3. 58

4. 307

5. 1,662

Hands On: Add and Subtract Fractions

CA Standards
KEY NS 3.2, MR 2.3

Add. Use fraction tiles to help.

1. $\frac{5}{7} + \frac{1}{7} =$

2. $\frac{4}{10} + \frac{4}{10} =$

3. $\frac{6}{9} + \frac{1}{9} =$

4. $\frac{1}{4} + \frac{1}{4} =$

5. $\frac{5}{11} + \frac{3}{11} =$

6. $\frac{2}{5} + \frac{1}{5} =$

Subtract. Use fraction tiles to help.

7. $\frac{4}{8} - \frac{1}{8} =$

8. $\frac{6}{12} - \frac{2}{12} =$

9. $\frac{3}{5} - \frac{2}{5} =$

10. $\frac{9}{10} - \frac{4}{10} =$

11. $\frac{7}{7} - \frac{6}{7} =$

12. $\frac{2}{4} - \frac{1}{4} =$

Test Practice

Circle the letter of the correct answer.

13. What is the sum of $\frac{3}{7} + \frac{4}{7}$?

   A $\frac{1}{7}$ B $\frac{6}{7}$ C $\frac{7}{7}$ D $\frac{5}{7}$

14. What is the difference of $\frac{4}{6} - \frac{1}{6}$?

   A $\frac{2}{6}$ B $\frac{3}{6}$ C $\frac{4}{6}$ D $\frac{5}{6}$

Writing Math Phil says that the sum of $\frac{2}{5}$ and $\frac{2}{5}$ is $\frac{2}{10}$. Is he right? Explain your reasoning.

_____

_____

_____

Add Fractions

Problem of the Day ————————— KEY NS 3.2

Hal has 12 markers. Three are red, 2 are green, and the rest are black. What fraction are not black? Show the addition sentence you use.

Measurement Review ————————— MG 1.1

Estimate the width of the classroom door in inches, feet, and yards.

Number of the Day ————————— KEY NS 1.5

817

Write the number in expanded form and word form.

_____

_____

_____

Facts Practice ————————— KEY NS 2.1

Add.

1. $72 + 29$

2. $343 + 76$

3. $273 + 228$

4. $608 + 147$

5. $126 + 355$

Name _____ Date _____

Add Fractions

CA Standards
KEY NS 3.2, NS 3.1

Add. Use fraction strips or draw a picture to help you.

1. $\frac{2}{5} + \frac{2}{5} =$ _____

2. $\frac{3}{6} + \frac{2}{6} =$ _____

3. $\frac{1}{3} + \frac{1}{3} =$ _____

4. $\frac{2}{4} + \frac{1}{4} =$ _____

5. $\frac{2}{8} + \frac{3}{8} =$ _____

6. $\frac{2}{4} + \frac{1}{4} =$ _____

7. $\frac{1}{5} + \frac{3}{5} =$ _____

8. $\frac{4}{6} + \frac{1}{6} =$ _____

9. $\frac{3}{9} + \frac{4}{9} =$ _____

Find the sum. Then find a fraction or whole number in the box below that is equivalent to the sum. Fractions or whole numbers may be used more than once.

10. $\frac{2}{10} + \frac{3}{10} =$ _____

11. $\frac{1}{6} + \frac{1}{6} =$ _____

12. $\frac{3}{4} + \frac{1}{4} =$ _____

13. $\frac{2}{8} + \frac{2}{8} =$ _____

14. $\frac{4}{10} + \frac{4}{10} =$ _____

15. $\frac{2}{12} + \frac{2}{12} =$ _____

$\frac{1}{3}, 1, \frac{1}{2}, \frac{3}{4}, \frac{4}{5}$

Test Practice

Circle the letter of the correct answer.

16. Find the sum of $\frac{1}{9}$ and $\frac{3}{9}$.

A $\frac{2}{9}$ C $\frac{4}{9}$

B $\frac{5}{9}$ D $\frac{6}{9}$

17. What is the value of n in this problem?

$$\frac{n}{8} + \frac{6}{8} = \frac{7}{8}$$

A 1   C 3

B 2   D 8

Writing Math In the problem $\frac{n}{9} + \frac{2}{9} = \frac{7}{9}$, what is the value of n? Explain how you got your answer.

_____

_____

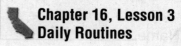

Name _____ Date _____

Subtract Fractions

Problem of the Day ———————————————————— KEY NS 3.2

Greg and Anton are painting a fence. Greg painted $\frac{2}{5}$ and Anton painted $\frac{3}{5}$. Did they finish the job? Explain.

Geometry Review ———————————————————— MG 2.5

Name four objects that have the shape of a cylinder.

Number of the Day ———————————————————— NS 1.2

1,234

Use the digits in 1,234 to make two different numbers. Use less than signs to show how the numbers are related.

_____

_____

_____

Facts Practice ———————————————————— KEY NS 2.1

Find each difference.

1. $93 - 13$

2. $145 - 63$

3. $458 - 21$

4. $374 - 180$

5. $59 - 23$

Name _____ Date _____

Subtract Fractions

CA Standards
KEY NS 3.2, NS 3.1

Use the picture to find the difference.

1.

$\frac{1}{6}$	$\frac{1}{6}$	✗			

$$\frac{3}{6} - \frac{1}{6} = \text{_____}$$

2.

$\frac{1}{5}$	$\frac{1}{5}$	$\frac{1}{5}$	✗	

$$\frac{4}{5} - \frac{2}{5} = \text{_____}$$

Subtract.

3. $\frac{6}{8} - \frac{1}{8} = \text{\_\_\_\_\_}$ 4. $\frac{5}{7} - \frac{3}{7} = \text{\_\_\_\_\_}$ 5. $\frac{4}{9} - \frac{1}{9} = \text{\_\_\_\_\_}$

6. $\frac{2}{6} - \frac{1}{6} = \text{\_\_\_\_\_}$ 7. $1 - \frac{2}{8} = \text{\_\_\_\_\_}$ 8. $\frac{9}{9} - \frac{7}{9} = \text{\_\_\_\_\_}$

9. $\frac{3}{5} - \frac{1}{5} = \text{\_\_\_\_\_}$ 10. $\frac{4}{6} - \frac{2}{6} = \text{\_\_\_\_\_}$ 11. $\frac{6}{10} - \frac{2}{10} = \text{\_\_\_\_\_}$

12. $\frac{5}{9} - \frac{1}{9} = \text{\_\_\_\_\_}$ 13. $\frac{4}{5} - \frac{1}{5} = \text{\_\_\_\_\_}$ 14. $\frac{2}{3} - \frac{1}{3} = \text{\_\_\_\_\_}$

Test Practice

Circle the letter of the correct answer.

15. Find $\frac{9}{10} - \frac{6}{10}$.

A $\frac{15}{10}$ C $\frac{3}{10}$

B $\frac{2}{10}$ D $\frac{0}{10}$

16. If you were given the problem $1 - \frac{2}{7}$, what would you change the 1 to?

A $\frac{5}{7}$ C $\frac{8}{7}$

B $\frac{7}{7}$ D $\frac{1}{7}$

 Writing Math Bill subtracted $\frac{2}{8}$ from $\frac{4}{8}$ and got $\frac{1}{4}$.
Explain how he got this answer.

_____

Practice Adding and Subtracting Fractions

Problem of the Day ————————————————

Jake has a piece of red fabric $\frac{9}{10}$ meter long. June has a piece of blue fabric $\frac{3}{10}$ meter long. How much longer is Jake's fabric?

Number Sense Review ————————————————

Write a number sentence you could use to solve the problem.

Tony sold 253 beaded bracelets at a craft show on Saturday. He sold another 148 on Sunday. How many beaded bracelets did he sell in all?

Word of the Day ————————————————

degree

Temperature is measured in degrees. What might the temperature be on a very hot day? On a very cold day?

_____

_____

_____

Facts Practice ————————————————

Find each product.

1. 7×4

2. 5×6

3. 3×9

4. 2×7

5. 4×8

Name _____ Date _____

Practice Adding and Subtracting Fractions

CA Standards
MR 1.2, **KEY** NS 3.2

Add or subtract.

1. $\dfrac{10}{11} - \dfrac{4}{11} =$ _____

2. $\dfrac{2}{2} - \dfrac{1}{2} =$ _____

3. $\dfrac{1}{6} + \dfrac{4}{6} =$ _____

4. $\dfrac{4}{10} + \dfrac{5}{10} =$ _____

5. $\dfrac{3}{4} - \dfrac{2}{4} =$ _____

6. $\dfrac{2}{7} + \dfrac{3}{7} =$ _____

Find the sum or difference. Then find a fraction or whole number in the box that is equivalent to the sum or difference. Fractions or whole numbers may be used more than once.

7. $\dfrac{2}{8} + \dfrac{4}{8} =$ _____

8. $\dfrac{6}{3} - \dfrac{3}{3} =$ _____

9. $\dfrac{12}{10} - \dfrac{8}{10} =$ _____

10. $\dfrac{9}{12} - \dfrac{3}{12} =$ _____

11. $\dfrac{9}{9} - \dfrac{3}{9} =$ _____

12. $\dfrac{4}{5} + \dfrac{1}{5} =$ _____

$$\dfrac{1}{2},\ \dfrac{2}{5},\ 1,\ \dfrac{2}{3},\ \dfrac{3}{4}$$

Test Practice

Circle the letter of the correct answer.

13. A cake is divided into nine parts. Sam ate $\dfrac{2}{9}$, Fred ate $\dfrac{1}{9}$, and Emmy ate $\dfrac{2}{9}$. How much cake was left?

   A $\dfrac{4}{9}$ C $\dfrac{6}{9}$

   B $\dfrac{5}{9}$ D $\dfrac{7}{9}$

14. Barbara hiked $\dfrac{3}{5}$ of the way to the top of the mountain. How much farther does she have to go to reach the top?

   A $\dfrac{1}{5}$ C $\dfrac{4}{5}$

   B $\dfrac{3}{5}$ D $\dfrac{2}{5}$

Writing Math Karl ate part of a pizza. There is $\dfrac{3}{4}$ of the pizza left. What must you do to find out how much Karl ate?

_____

_____

Problem Solving: Field Trip

Problem of the Day
KEY NS 3.2

Mei used $\frac{3}{8}$ pound of Swiss cheese and $\frac{2}{8}$ pound cheddar cheese to make fondue. John used $\frac{3}{5}$ pound of Swiss cheese and $\frac{2}{5}$ pound cheddar cheese to make fondue. Who used more cheese?

Geometry Review
KEY MG 2.1

What kind of polygon do you get if you cut off two opposite corners of a rectangle?

Number of the Day
KEY NS 2.2

48

Write all the multiplication facts you know that equal 48.

_____

_____

_____

Facts Practice
NS 2.5

Divide.

1. $48 \div 6$

2. $28 \div 4$

3. $45 \div 9$

4. $30 \div 5$

5. $32 \div 8$

Hands On: Tenths and Hundredths

Problem of the Day ———————————————— MR 1.0

A long mural has 16 equal sections. Shari and her friends paint 5 sections. Don's team paints $\frac{1}{4}$ of the mural. Have the two groups painted more or less than $\frac{1}{2}$ of the mural? Explain.

Geometry Review ———————————————— KEY MG 2.2

What do you get if you cut an equilateral triangle in half along a line through one vertex?

Number of the Day ———————————————— MG 1.1

12

Use three different units of length with the number 12. Name something that has each length.

_____

_____

_____

Facts Practice ———————————————— NS 1.4

Round each number to the nearest hundred.

1. 894

2. 3,207

3. 618

4. 4,106

5. 89

Name _____ Date _____

Hands On: Tenths and Hundredths

CA Standards
NS 3.0, NS 3.1

Model the fraction.

1. $\frac{2}{10}$

2. $\frac{7}{10}$

3. $\frac{4}{10}$

4. $\frac{24}{100}$

5. $\frac{46}{100}$

6. $\frac{4}{100}$

7. $\frac{70}{100}$

8. $\frac{63}{100}$

9. $\frac{81}{100}$

Test Practice

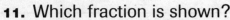

Circle the letter of the correct answer.

10. Which fraction is shown?

   A $\frac{5}{10}$ C $\frac{60}{100}$

   B $\frac{5}{100}$ D $\frac{6}{100}$

11. Which fraction is shown?

   A $\frac{14}{100}$ C $\frac{24}{100}$

   B $\frac{34}{100}$ D $\frac{44}{100}$

 Writing Math Is $\frac{50}{100}$ greater than $\frac{5}{10}$? Explain.

_____

_____

Name _____ Date _____

Tenths Practice

Problem of the Day ———————————————————— NS 3.0

Petra ran 0.7 of a mile. What fraction of a mile did she run?

Number Sense Review ———————————————————— NS 2.0

Maggie puts 4 pompoms on each puppet she makes. In all, she used 28 pompoms. Draw a picture to show how many puppets Maggie made. Write a number sentence that tells how many puppets she made.

Word of the Day ———————————————————— KEY **AF 1.1**

equal

Write a sentence that uses the word *equal*. Find at least two other words that begin with the prefix *equ-*.

_____

_____

_____

Facts Practice ———————————————————— KEY **NS 2.1**

Subtract.

1. $153 - 18$

2. $494 - 128$

3. $72 - 39$

4. $263 - 47$

5. $81 - 35$

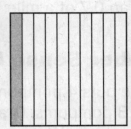
Tenths

Write a fraction and a decimal for the shaded part.

1. 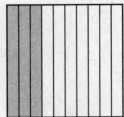   **2.** 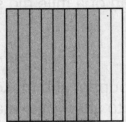   **3.**

_____   _____   _____

Write as a decimal.

4. $\dfrac{2}{10}$ **5.** $\dfrac{5}{10}$ **6.** three tenths   **7.** six tenths

_____   _____   _____   _____

Write as a fraction.

8. 0.8   **9.** 0.4   **10.** one tenth   **11.** seven tenths

_____   _____   _____   _____

 **Test Practice**

Circle the letter of the correct answer.

12. Which decimal equals nine tenths?

   A 0.9   **C** 0.09

   B 9.0   **D** 0.99

13. Which fraction equals 0.7?

   A $\dfrac{1}{7}$ **C** $\dfrac{7}{1}$

   B $\dfrac{7}{10}$ **D** $\dfrac{7}{100}$

 Writing Math Which is greater, $\dfrac{5}{10}$ or 0.5? Explain.

_____

_____

Daily Routines and Practice

172

Use with text pp. 368–369

Hundredths

Problem of the Day ———————————— NS 3.4

Lyle bought 0.3 pounds of nuts. Barb bought $\frac{1}{2}$ pound. Who bought more? Explain.

Measurement Review ———————————— MG 1.1

Name some objects that are between 20 and 30 centimeters long.

Number of the Day ———————————— NS 3.0

60

There are 60 minutes in an hour. How many minutes are in a quarter-hour? In a half-hour?

_____

_____

_____

Facts Practice ———————————— KEY

Find each sum.

1. 45 + 21 + 16

2. 32 + 9 + 74

3. 18 + 40 + 31

4. 7 + 29 + 63

5. 14 + 97 + 82

Hundredths

CA Standards
NS 3.4, NS 3.0

Write a fraction and a decimal for the shaded part.

1.

2.

3.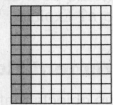

_____   _____   _____

Write as a decimal.

4. $\frac{30}{100}$

5. $\frac{6}{100}$

6. $\frac{57}{100}$

7. seventeen hundredths

_____   _____   _____

Write as a fraction.

8. 0.12

9. 0.08

10. 0.72

11. ninety hundredths

_____   _____   _____   _____

Test Practice

Circle the letter of the correct answer.

12. Which decimal equals $\frac{5}{100}$?

   A 05.0   **B** 0.05   **C** 0.5   **D** 5.0

13. Which fraction equals 0.63?

   A $\frac{10}{63}$ **B** $\frac{63}{10}$ **C** $\frac{63}{100}$ **D** $\frac{100}{63}$

 Writing Math What does the 0 after the decimal point in 0.06 show?

_____

Relate Fractions, Decimals, and Money

Problem of the Day — NS 3.4

Nine centimeters is 0.09 meter. What part of a meter is 90 centimeters? Write the answer as both a fraction and a decimal.

Algebra Review — AF 1.3

Use the numbers 3, 4, 5, and 6 and the symbols +, ×, and < to make a true inequality.

Number of the Day — NS 1.1

313

If you count by threes, will you name 313? Why or why not?

_____

_____

_____

Facts Practice — KEY NS 2.2

Multiply.

1. 7×6

2. 2×3

3. 0×9

4. 8×2

5. 5×4

Hands On: Relate Fractions, Decimals, and Money

CA Standards
NS 3.4, NS 3.0

Complete the table. Use coins to help you.

	Coins	Number of Cents	Fraction of a Dollar	Values as a Decimal
1.	7 pennies			
2.	6 dimes			
3.	3 quarters			

Write the amount as a fraction of a dollar.

4. $0.35 = _____ of a dollar

5. $0.81 = _____ of a dollar

6. $0.09 = _____ of a dollar

7. $0.70 = _____ of a dollar

8. $0.10 = _____ of a dollar

9. $0.97 = _____ of a dollar

10. $0.30 = _____ of a dollar

11. $0.05 = _____ of a dollar

Test Practice

Circle the letter of the correct answer.

12. Which amount equals 2 quarters?

   A $0.05   C $0.50

   B $0.25   D $25.00

13. Which amount equals 8 dimes?

   A $0.80   C $8.00

   B $0.08   D $80.00

Writing Math Which is worth more, 40 pennies or 1 half-dollar? Explain.

_____

_____

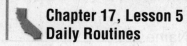
Problem Solving: Reasonable Answers

Problem of the Day ———————————————————————— NS 3.4

Which is greater, $\frac{3}{4}$ of a dollar or 70 cents? Explain how
you know.

Number Sense Review ————————————————————— KEY NS 2.1

There were 854 students in the state science fair. If 476 were
girls, how many were boys?

Number of the Day ————————————————————————— NS 1.4

90

A number rounded to the nearest ten equals 90. What is the
greatest number that rounds to 90?

_____

_____

_____

Facts Practice ————————————————————————————— NS 2.5

Find each quotient.

1. $3\overline{)27}$

2. $8\overline{)56}$

3. $5\overline{)35}$

4. $9\overline{)72}$

5. $6\overline{)48}$

Reasonable Answers

CA Standards
MR 3.1, NS 3.4

Tell whether the answer is reasonable. Then solve the problem and tell if the answer is correct.

1. Duane baked two apple pies. He cut each pie into 4 equal slices. Members of his family have eaten 3 slices. What fraction shows how much of the two pies is left? Duane answers: $\frac{5}{8}$

_____

2. A container held 0.5 of one cup of orange juice. Another container held 0.25 of one cup of grapefruit juice. What is the difference in amount of juice in the two containers? Answer: **There is 0.25 of a cup more juice in the grapefruit juice container.**

_____

3. Cruz has $1.35, and his sister is hoping to borrow a half dollar from him. If Cruz lends her this money, how much money will he have left? Cruz answers: **$1.35**

_____

Test Practice

Circle the letter of the correct answer.

4. A gas can has 0.3 of one gallon of gas in it. If the can holds 2 gallons in all, how much gas can be added to the can?

   A 0.7 of a gallon

   B 1.3 gallons

   C 1.7 gallons

   D 2 gallons

5. Stephen has $1.90 saved up. Then he earns $0.75 in one week. How much money does he have in all?

   A $1.25

   B $1.90

   C $1.45

   D $2.65

Writing Math What operation did you use to solve problem 4 and to solve problem 5?

_____

_____

Hands On: Add and Subtract Money Amounts

Problem of the Day ——————————————————— MR 3.1

Solve. Decide whether the answer is reasonable or not.

Kelly and Sandra each ate $\frac{2}{5}$ of a pizza. They say they have $\frac{1}{2}$ of the pizza left. Is this reasonable?

Measurement Review ——————————————— KEY (MG 1.3)

What is the distance around a square park that is 30 meters on each side?

Number of the Day ——————————————————— KEY (NS 2.1)

20

Show 20 as the sum of four odd numbers.

_____

_____

_____

Facts Practice ————————————————————————— NS 1.4

Round each number to the greatest place.

1. 371

2. 83

3. 129

4. 883

5. 743

Hands On: Add and Subtract Money Amounts

CA Standards
KEY NS 3.3, MR 2.0

Use the table and play money to solve the problems.

1. Ethan bought a binder and a ruler. How much did he spend in all?

_____

Item	Cost
Binder	$4.35
Ruler	$1.48
Glue	$2.66
Index Cards	$1.60

2. What is the total cost of 2 binders?

_____

3. How much more does glue cost than index cards?

_____

4. How much less does a ruler cost than glue?

_____

5. Isamu had $6.30. He bought index cards. How much money does he have left?

_____

6. Nora had $5.90. She bought a ruler. How much money does she have left?

_____

Test Practice

Circle the letter of the correct answer.

7. Marco had $8.50 to buy a book that costs $6.63. How much change does he get back?

   A $1.87   B $2.87   C $1.78   D $2.78

8. Tracy bought a pen that costs $1.39 and a notebook that costs $3.82. How much did he spend in all?

   A $4.21   B $5.21   C $4.11   D $5.11

Writing Math If you had $8.00 to buy stamps that cost $3.90, how much change would you receive? Explain.

_____

Add Money Amounts

Problem of the Day ——————————————— KEY NS 3.3

Tony saved $1.90 last week. This week, he added two dimes to his savings. How much did Tony save in all?

Number Sense Review ——————————————— KEY NS 1.5

Write 4,073 in expanded form.

Number of the Day ——————————————— NS 3.1

$\frac{1}{4}$

Throughout the school day, use the fraction $\frac{1}{4}$ to describe some situations.

_____

_____

_____

Facts Practice ——————————————— KEY NS 2.1

Find each difference.

1. $2{,}064 - 825$

2. $1{,}375 - 462$

3. $5{,}677 - 1{,}342$

4. $4{,}621 - 1{,}708$

Add Money Amounts

Add.

1. $3.62 + $2.10 =

2. $0.83 + $2.81 =

3. $7.84 + $3.91 =

_____

_____

_____

4. $52.07 + $31.89 =

5. $7.49 + $4.55 =

_____

_____

6. $65.83 + $14.76 =

7. $3.22 + $1.61 + $5.00 =

_____

_____

8. $3.11 + $1.63 + $2.81 =

9. $5.30 + $2.73 + $4.04 =

_____

_____

Test Practice

Circle the letter of the correct answer.

10. Yoshio bought a ball that cost $4.36, a hat that cost $5.19, and a pack of gum that cost $0.74. What was the total cost of these three items?

   A $9.39   B $10.39   C $9.29   D $10.29

11. Grace bought a pack of cards for $2.78, a key chain for $3.65, and a jump rope for $5.15. What was the total cost of these three items?

   A $11.48   B $12.48   C $11.58   D $12.58

Writing Math Eric added $4.76 and $1.32. He wrote his answer as $608. What did he do wrong? Explain.

_____

Subtract Money Amounts

Problem of the Day ——————————————————— KEY NS 3.3

Emilio spent $12 for a model car kit and $8 for paint. Then his grandfather gave him $10. Now he has $14. How much money did Emilio have before he went shopping?

Functions Review ————————————————————— AF 2.2

Isabella measured the height of a plant on the fifth day after she planted a seed. It was 2 centimeters tall. On day 7 it was 5 centimeters tall, and on day 9 it was 8 centimeters tall. At this rate, when will the plant be 20 centimeters tall? Show the pattern in a table.

Number of the Day ————————————————————— NS 1.1

36

What are some ways to show 36?

_____

_____

_____

Facts Practice ————————————————————— KEY NS 2.1

Add or subtract.

1. $34 + 12 + 60$

2. $85 - 29$

3. $75 + 93$

4. $18 + 9 + 36$

5. $73 - 28$

Subtract Money Amounts

CA Standards
KEY NS 3.3, MR 3.2

Subtract. Check by adding.

1. $7.80 − $6.30 =

_____

2. $7.84 − $3.91 =

_____

3. $6.97 − $5.88 =

_____

4. $8.55 − $2.09 =

_____

5. $64.21 − $20.54 =

_____

6. $43.18 − $36.66 =

_____

7. $85.00 − $47.43 =

_____

8. $70.00 − $36.89 =

_____

9. $92.11 − $23.45 =

_____

 **Test Practice**

Circle the letter of the correct answer.

10. Carmen had $10.00 to buy a scarf that cost $7.25. How much change should she get back?

   A $2.75   B $3.75   C $2.85   D $3.85

11. Martel had $9.50 to buy gloves that cost $6.68. How much change should he get back?

   A $3.82   B $2.82   C $3.92   D $2.92

Writing Math Lacey subtracted $4.17 from $10.00. She wrote her answer as 5.83. What did she do wrong? Explain.

_____

_____

Name _____   Date _____

Function Tables and Money

Problem of the Day ——————————————————— KEY NS 3.3

Toby earned $10.00 doing chores. He spent $6.50 on a movie
ticket and $3.25 on snacks. How much money does he have left?

Number Sense Review ——————————————— KEY NS 2.2

Draw a picture to show 3 rows of 5 flags each. Write a number
sentence that tells how many flags there are in all.

Word of the Day ————————————————————— MG 1.0

measure

Name some situations in which you measure something during
the school day.

_____

_____

_____

Facts Practice ————————————————————— NS 2.5

Divide.

1. 4)‾36‾

2. 8)‾40‾

3. 5)‾50‾

4. 9)‾63‾

5. 6)‾36‾

Function Tables and Money

CA Standards
KEY AF 2.1, 2.0

Find the function rule and complete the function table.

1.

Input	Output
$4.00	
$3.00	$2.30
$1.90	
$0.90	$0.20

_____

2.

Input	Output
$1.00	
$1.50	$3.70
$2.00	
$2.50	$4.70

_____

3.

Input	Output
2	
3	$18.00
4	
5	$30.00

_____

4.

Input	Output
$9.00	
$15.00	$5.00
$24.00	
$27.00	$9.00

_____

5.

Input	Output
$3.00	
$5.23	$9.23
$7.44	
$9.02	$13.02

_____

6.

Input	Output
$5.00	
$6.45	$3.15
$8.52	
$9.60	$6.30

_____

✓ Test Practice

Circle the letter of the correct answer.

7. For 7-8 use the table. How much would 4 pens cost?

Number of pens	Cost
1	$2.00
2	$4.00
3	$6.00

   A $7.00   **C** $8.00

   B $9.00   **D** $10.00

8. How much would 6 pens cost?

   A $12.00   **B** $14.00   **C** $13.00   **D** $15.00

Writing Math You are given a function table that has a multiplication or division rule. How will you know which operation was used? Explain.

_____

_____

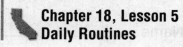
Problem Solving: Write a Number Sentence

Problem of the Day ———————————————— KEY NS 3.3

A carpenter bought 8 pounds of nails. The price of the nails was
$3.95 per pound. About how much did the nails cost?

Geometry Review ————————————————————— MG 2.5

The bottom of a pyramid is a rectangle. How many edges does
this pyramid have?

Number of the Day ————————————————————— AF 1.2

30

Find two different two-digit numbers that make this inequality
true: $A + B < 30$

_____

_____

_____

Facts Practice ——————————————————————— KEY NS 2.2

Find each product.

1. 8×9

2. 10×4

3. 6×7

4. 8×3

5. 3×11

Name _____ Date _____

Write a Number Sentence

**Write a number sentence to solve each problem. Explain why
your answer makes sense.**

1. Owen wishes to buy two packages of sports cards. One has a price of $2.95,
and the other costs $3.25. How much would the two packages cost in all?

   _____

2. Natalie and her parents wish to buy a gallon of orange juice. One brand sells a
gallon for $3.49. Another brand sells a gallon for $4.79. What is the difference
in price between these two gallons of orange juice?

   _____

3. A man gets $6.29 in change from a store. He already has $2.77 in his pocket.
How much money now does he have in all?

   _____

4. Mrs. Miller's change purse contains $7.48 in coins. At a store, she uses $6.89 of
these coins to pay for snacks. How much change does she have left in her purse?

   _____

Test Practice

Circle the letter of the correct answer.

5. Harrison earned $1.20 and added
it to his savings of $4.82. How
much money does Harrison have
in all?

   A $4.82   c $5.82

   B $5.92   D $6.02

6. Yolanda earned $4.00 during one
month. Then she was able to pay her
sister the $2.85 she owed her. How
much money does Yolanda have left?

   A $1.15   c $1.25

   B $2.15   D 2.25

Writing Math Why is the thousandths place not used
when writing amounts of dollars and cents?

_____

_____

Hands On: Multiplication Patterns with 10, 100, and 1,000

Problem of the Day
KEY **AF 1.1**

Write a number sentence to solve.

Suki makes bracelets. She puts 12 beads on each bracelet.
How many beads will she use for 4 bracelets?

Number Sense Review
KEY **NS 1.5**

During one year, Max sold 3,024 bags of oranges at his produce
market. Write this number in expanded form.

Number of the Day
KEY **NS 1.3**

21.12

What digit is in the hundredths place? Use the digits 1 and 2 to
write another two-place decimal. Is this decimal greater than or
less than 21.12?

_____

_____

_____

Facts Practice
NS 1.4

Round each number to the nearest thousand.

1. 4,326

2. 5,103

3. 8,747

4. 1,225

5. 3,562

Hands On: Multiplication Patterns with 10, 100, and 1,000

CA Standards
KEY NS 2.4, MR 1.1

Use a basic fact and patterns to find the product.

1. $4 \times 3 =$ _____
$4 \times 30 =$ _____
$4 \times 300 =$ _____
$4 \times 3{,}000 =$ _____

2. $5 \times 2 =$ _____
$5 \times 20 =$ _____
$5 \times 200 =$ _____
$5 \times 2{,}000 =$ _____

3. $7 \times 4 =$ _____
$7 \times 40 =$ _____
$7 \times 400 =$ _____
$7 \times 4{,}000 =$ _____

4. $2 \times 2 =$ _____
$2 \times 20 =$ _____
$2 \times 200 =$ _____
$2 \times 2{,}000 =$ _____

5. $5 \times 5 =$ _____
$5 \times 50 =$ _____
$5 \times 500 =$ _____
$5 \times 5{,}000 =$ _____

6. $9 \times 4 =$ _____
$9 \times 40 =$ _____
$9 \times 400 =$ _____
$9 \times 4{,}000 =$ _____

7. $3 \times 5 =$ _____
$3 \times 50 =$ _____
$3 \times 500 =$ _____
$3 \times 5{,}000 =$ _____

8. $8 \times 7 =$ _____
$8 \times 70 =$ _____
$8 \times 700 =$ _____
$8 \times 7{,}000 =$ _____

9. $3 \times 3 =$ _____
$3 \times 30 =$ _____
$3 \times 300 =$ _____
$3 \times 3{,}000 =$ _____

Test Practice

Circle the letter of the correct answer.

10. Which fact helps you compute 3×200?

A $3 \times 2 = 6$
B $3 \times 3 = 9$
C $3 \times 5 = 15$
D $3 \times 10 = 30$

11. Complete the pattern:
$5 \times 6 = 30$
$5 \times 60 = 300$
$5 \times \boxed{} = 3{,}000$

A 60
B 600
C 6,000
D 60,000

 Writing Math Explain how to use a pattern and the fact $5 \times 4 = 20$ to compute the product of 5×400.

_____

_____

Multiply with Multiples of 10, 100, or 1,000

Problem of the Day ——————————————————— MR 1.1

Pencils come in boxes of 10, 100, and 1,000. Mr. Dobson needs
1,000 pencils. If he buys only boxes of the same size, how many
boxes of each size would he need?

Algebra Review ———————————————————— KEY **AF 1.1**

Jana biked 12 miles on Saturday. Hank biked 3 times as far.
Write a number sentence that you could use to find how many
miles Hank biked.

Number of the Day ———————————————————— KEY **NS 1.5**

40,702

Write the expanded notation. Which places have a value of zero?

_____

_____

_____

Facts Practice ———————————————————— KEY **NS 2.1**

Subtract.

1. 743 − 68   2. 2,108 − 430

3. 1,755 − 108   4. 932 − 187

Multipy with Multiples of 10, 100, or 1,000

CA Standards
KEY NS 2.4, MR 1.1

Use a basic fact and patterns to help you find the product.

1. $7 \times 20 =$ _____

2. $2 \times 60 =$ _____

3. $3 \times 50 =$ _____

4. $5 \times 80 =$ _____

5. $9 \times 400 =$ _____

6. $3 \times 700 =$ _____

7. $7 \times 400 =$ _____

8. $3 \times 500 =$ _____

9. $2 \times 9,000 =$ _____

10. $9 \times 6,000 =$ _____

11. $8 \times 9,000 =$ _____

12. $6 \times 4,000 =$ _____

Test Practice

Circle the letter of the correct answer.

13. What is the product of 4×400?

 A 16   c 160

 B 16,000   D 1,600

14. What is the product of 8×700?

 A 56   c 5,600

 B 560   D 56,000

 Writing Math Explain how you know the product of 6×700 given $6 \times 7 = 42$.

_____

_____

Estimate Products

Problem of the Day ————————————————————— KEY NS 2.4

Charlie bought 4 boxes of paper clips. Each box holds 800 paper clips. How many paper clips did he buy in all?

Number Sense Review ————————————————————— KEY NS 3.3

Sarita bought a notebook for $3.79. She paid with a $5 bill. How much change did she receive?

Word of the Day ————————————————————————— MG 2.0

right

Use the word *right* as an adjective in as many ways as you can.

_____

_____

_____

Facts Practice ——————————————————————————— KEY NS 3.3

Find each difference.

1. $7.45 − $2.30

2. $6.23 − $1.80

3. $3.50 − $0.84

4. $15.25 − $7.30

5. $23.40 − $12.83

Estimate Products

CA Standard
KEY MR 2.5

Estimate the product. Round the larger factor to its greatest place.

1. 47×5 2. 56×6 3. 324×3 4. 699×8

_____   _____   _____   _____

5. 32×6 6. 719×2 7. 589×8 8. 425×8

_____   _____   _____   _____

Compare. Write >, <, or = for each ◯.

9. 61×5 ◯ 38×3 10. 30×3 ◯ 9×12 11. 4×40 ◯ 80×2

12. 153×4 ◯ 163×4 13. 3×20 ◯ 20×3 14. 60×6 ◯ 5×60

 **Test Practice**

Circle the letter of the correct answer.

15. Which is the best estimate of 294×5?

  A 1,600   C 150

  B 15,000   D 1,500

16. Janet has 5 photo albums with 38 photos in each album. About how many photos does she have?

  A 15   C 200

  B 150   D 400

Writing Math Estimate to decide if 28×6 is greater than or less than 28×5. Explain your answer.

_____

Problem Solving: Field Trip

Problem of the Day ———————————————— MR 2.5

Brian and Jake each have 37 model cars. About how many model cars do they have in all?

Measurement Review ———————————————— MG 1.1

Geraldine has 2.3 meters of red ribbon and 800 centimeters of white ribbon. Write the total length of ribbon in both centimeters and meters.

Number of the Day ———————————————— KEY NS 2.3

8

Write four different multiplication and division sentences that include 8.

_____

_____

_____

Facts Practice ———————————————————— KEY NS 2.2

Find each product.

1. 9×6

2. 5×4

3. 7×8

4. 2×6

5. 3×5

Hands On: Multiply 2-Digit Numbers

Problem of the Day ——————————————— AF 2.2

Make a table to solve the problem..

Kelli is learning to tie fancy knots. She learned 4 knots the first week. Each week after, she learned 3 more knots. How many knots had she learned after 5 weeks?

Number Sense Review ————————————— KEY NS 1.5

Mia wrote this expression to represent a number.

$$50,000 + 1,000 + 400 + 20$$

Write the standard form of this number.

Word of the Day ——————————————— MG 1.0

meter

Write some units of measure and other words that end in *-meter*.

_____

_____

_____

Facts Practice ——————————————— NS 1.4

Round each number to the nearest hundred.

1. 463

2. 5,071

3. 182

4. 3,442

5. 7,465

Hands On: Multiply Two-Digit Numbers

CA Standards
KEY NS 2.4, MR 2.3

Tell what multiplication sentence is shown by the blocks.

1. $2 \times 31 =$ _____

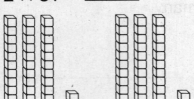

2. $3 \times 12 =$ _____

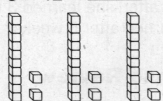

Use base-ten blocks to help you find the product.

3. $4 \times 22 =$ _____

4. $3 \times 31 =$ _____

5. $4 \times 12 =$ _____

6. $2 \times 13 =$ _____

7. $3 \times 23 =$ _____

8. $2 \times 34 =$ _____

 **Test Practice**

Circle the letter of the correct answer.

9. Tonya wants to use base-ten blocks to show 2×33. What should she do?

   A make 3 groups of 33

   B make 2 groups of 33

   C make 3 groups of tens

   D make 3 groups of ones

10. Terry wants to show 4×21 using base-ten blocks. What will he need?

    A 2 groups of 2 tens and 2 ones

    B 2 groups of 4 tens and 1 ones

    C 4 groups of 2 tens and 1 ones

    D 4 groups of 1 tens and 2 ones

Writing Math How can you use base-ten blocks to multiply 13 by 3?

_____

_____

_____

Multiply 2-Digit Numbers

Problem of the Day ————————————————— KEY NS 2.4

An apartment building had 21 apartments with 5 rooms in each
one. Every room has a smoke detector in it. Use base-ten blocks
to help you figure out the total number of smoke detectors in the
apartment building.

Measurement Review ———————————————— MG 1.0

Marge walks 20 minutes each day. How many hours will she
spend walking in a 30-day month?

Number of the Day ———————————————————— NS 1.1

700

What are different ways you can represent 700?

_____

_____

_____

Facts Practice ———————————————————— KEY NS 3.3

Find each sum.

1. $1.80 + $0.35   2. $2.60 + $8.45   3. $3.77 + $1.79

4. $8.26 + $0.73   5. $5.90 + $2.70 + $3.50

Multiply 2-Digit Numbers

CA Standard
KEY NS 2.4

Multiply.

1. 21
    × 3

2. 11
    × 4

3. 24
    × 2

4. 13
    × 3

5. 21
    × 4

6. 33
    × 3

7. $32 \times 2 =$ _____

8. $30 \times 3 =$ _____

9. $10 \times 4 =$ _____

10. $2 \times 33 =$ _____

11. $11 \times 8 =$ _____

12. $42 \times 2 =$ _____

 **Test Practice**

Circle the letter of the correct answer.

13. Garrett wants to know the product of 3×23. Which two multiplication sentences will help him find the product?

    A $2 \times 3 = \square$ and $3 \times 2 = \square$

    B $3 \times 3 = \square$ and $2 \times 2 = \square$

    C $3 \times 3 = \square$ and $3 \times 2 = \square$

    D $3 \times 1 = \square$ and $3 \times 2 = \square$

14. Mike wants to know the product of 2×34. What is the first thing he should do?

    A Subtract 2 from 4.

    B Add 2 and 4.

    C Multiply the tens.

    D Multiply the ones.

 Writing Math Nell says the product of 4×21 is 48. What did Nell do wrong?

_____

_____

_____

Hands On: Regroup in Multiplication

Problem of the Day ———————————— KEY NS 2.4

Shelly earns $42 each week babysitting. About how much will she earn in 4 weeks?

Number Sense Review ———————————— NS 2.5

Jamie mows 15 lawns in 3 days. If he mows the same number of lawns each day, how many does he mow each day? Write a number sentence to show your answer.

Number of the Day ———————————— NS 3.1

$\frac{1}{2}$

Throughout the school day, use the fraction $\frac{1}{2}$ to describe some situations.

_____

_____

_____

Facts Practice ———————————— KEY NS 2.1

Add or subtract.

1. $8 + 15 + 33$ 2. $62 - 19$

3. $13 + 40 + 18$ 4. $74 - 30$

Hands On: Regroup in Multiplication

CA Standards
KEY NS 2.4, MR 2.1

Use base-ten blocks to help you find the product.

1. $4 \times 18 =$ _____

2. $6 \times 13 =$ _____

3. $5 \times 15 =$ _____

4. $2 \times 23 =$ _____

5. $5 \times 17 =$ _____

6. $4 \times 15 =$ _____

7. $3 \times 17 =$ _____

8. $2 \times 28 =$ _____

9. $5 \times 18 =$ _____

10. $6 \times 15 =$ _____

Tell what multiplication sentence is shown by the blocks.

11. _____

12. _____

Test Practice

Circle the letter of the correct answer.

13. Find 12×5.

A 50
B 60
C 65
D 61

14. How much greater is the product of 3 and 26 than the product of 2 and 26?

A 1
B 26
C 62
D 52

 Writing Math Jeremy is going to use base-ten blocks to find the product of 4 and 13. Tell him how to arrange the blocks.

_____

_____

_____

Name _____ Date _____

Regroup in Multiplication

Problem of the Day —————————————————— KEY NS 2.4

A rollercoaster has 8 cars. Each car can hold 12 people. What is the greatest number of people that can ride the rollercoaster at the same time?

Geometry Review ———————————————————————— MG 2.0

What kinds of line segments are modeled by railroad tracks?

Number of the Day ——————————————————————— NS 1.1

1,250

Write this number in words in two different ways.

_____

_____

_____

Facts Practice ———————————————————————— KEY NS 2.4

Multiply.

1. 30 × 6

2. 7 × 40

3. 80 × 5

4. 2 × 90

5. 60 × 3

Regroup in Multiplication

CA Standards
KEY NS 2.4, MR 2.1

Find the product.

1. $18 \times 4 = $ _____   2. $4 \times 14 = $ _____   3. $3 \times 18 = $ _____   4. $14 \times 6 = $ _____

5. $22 \times 4 = $ _____   6. $3 \times 14 = $ _____   7. $5 \times 15 = $ _____   8. $2 \times 46 = $ _____

Find the product.

9. $\begin{array}{r} 14 \\ \times\ 5 \\ \hline \end{array}$ 10. $\begin{array}{r} 11 \\ \times\ 5 \\ \hline \end{array}$ 11. $\begin{array}{r} 10 \\ \times\ 5 \\ \hline \end{array}$

12. $\begin{array}{r} 11 \\ \times\ 4 \\ \hline \end{array}$ 13. $\begin{array}{r} 23 \\ \times\ 4 \\ \hline \end{array}$ 14. $\begin{array}{r} 17 \\ \times\ 4 \\ \hline \end{array}$

15. $\begin{array}{r} 16 \\ \times\ 6 \\ \hline \end{array}$ 16. $\begin{array}{r} 12 \\ \times\ 6 \\ \hline \end{array}$ 17. $\begin{array}{r} 10 \\ \times\ 6 \\ \hline \end{array}$

✓ Test Practice

Circle the letter of the correct answer.

18. Sheri is making copies of a class book about Gutenberg's printing press. The book has 8 pages. She wants to make a copy of the book for her 12 classmates. How many pages will she copy in all?

   A 76   c 96

   B 90   D 100

19. Find the product of 3 and 26.

   A 68   c 78

   B 82   D 86

 Writing Math Loni is trying to find the product of 17 and 4. She has multiplied 7 and 4 and knows there are 28 ones. What should she do next?

_____

_____

Name _____ Date _____

Problem Solving: Use a Simpler Problem

Problem of the Day ————————————————— KEY NS 2.4

A class of 27 students went on a field trip to a science museum. The admission price for each student was $5. What was the total cost of admission for the students?

Number Sense Review ————————————————— NS 3.1

Which fraction does point *F* represent on this number line?

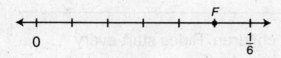

Number of the Day ————————————————— NS 3.1

24

Find $\frac{1}{2}$, $\frac{1}{3}$, $\frac{1}{4}$, $\frac{1}{6}$, and $\frac{1}{8}$ of 24. Draw models if you need to.

_____

_____

Facts Practice ————————————————— NS 2.5

Find each quotient.

1. $7\overline{)35}$

2. $8\overline{)64}$

3. $6\overline{)42}$

4. $3\overline{)24}$

5. $9\overline{)54}$

Use a Simpler Problem

CA Standards
MR 2.2, KEY NS 2.4

Solve. Explain why your answer makes sense.

1. A roller coaster can give a ride to 96 people in 30 minutes. How many people can ride the roller coaster in 2 hours?

   _____

2. The roller coaster can hold 48 people. There were 7 empty seats on the first ride, 13 empty seats on the second ride, 6 empty seats on the third ride, and 3 empty seats on the fourth ride. How many people rode on these four rides?

   _____

3. The roller coaster has 8 cars. Each car holds 6 children. Rides start every 15 minutes. How many children can ride in 60 minutes?

   _____

4. The roller coaster's track is 290 yards long. If each ride takes you around the track twice, how far would you travel during 4 rides?

   _____

Test Practice

Circle the letter of the correct answer.

5. A child needs 3 blue tickets to ride the Ferris wheel, and an adult needs 2 red tickets to ride it. If 29 children and 12 adults ride the Ferris wheel, how many tickets are collected in all?

   A 24   c 63

   B 87   D 111

6. During an afternoon, 138 children and 89 adults ride the Ferris wheel. What is the difference in the total number of red tickets and blue tickets collected?

   A 414   c 236

   B 178   D 138

Writing Math Explain the steps you took to find the answer to problem #3.

_____

_____

_____

Hands On: Multiply Greater Numbers

Problem of the Day ——————————————— MR 2.2

Use easier numbers to first solve a simpler problem. Show the simpler problem you use.

A train has 8 passenger cars. Four of the cars can each seat 68 riders. The other cars can seat 37 riders. How many people can ride the train at once?

Number Sense Review ——————————————— NS 3.1

Compare the fractions.

1. Which is greater: 3 robins in a group of 5 birds, or 4 blue jays in a group of 8 birds?

2. Which is greater: 6 red cards in a group of 10 cards, or 8 blue cards in a group of 12 cards?

Number of the Day ——————————————— KEY NS 3.3

$4.65

If something costs $4.65, how much change will you get from $5? from $10?

_____

_____

Facts Practice ——————————————— NS 1.4

Round each number to the nearest ten.

1. 93   2. 482   3. 5,643

4. 809   5. 346

Hands On: Multiply Greater Numbers

CA Standard
KEY NS 2.4

Use base-ten blocks to help you find the product.

1. $6 \times 113 =$ _____

2. $3 \times 226 =$ _____

3. $5 \times 106 =$ _____

4. $2 \times 348 =$ _____

5. $4 \times 135 =$ _____

6. $3 \times 316 =$ _____

7. $4 \times 204 =$ _____

8. $6 \times 119 =$ _____

9. $3 \times 263 =$ _____

10. $4 \times 162 =$ _____

Test Practice

11. A dragonfly has 4 wings. How many wings do 125 dragonflies have in all?

A 400

B 490

C 500

D 590

12. A frog has 4 legs. How many legs do 234 frogs have in all?

A 936

B 966

C 1,016

D 1,036

Writing Math Linden wants to find 5×117. Explain how to show this problem using base-ten blocks.

_____

_____

_____

Multiply a 3-Digit Number by a 1-Digit Number

Problem of the Day —————————————— KEY NS 2.4

There are 365 days in most years. About how many days are there in 5 years?

Geometry Review —————————————— KEY MG 1.2

What is the area of this house?

Number of the Day —————————————— KEY NS 2.1

679

Reverse the digits of the number. Find the sum and difference of the two 3-digit numbers.

_____

_____

_____

Facts Practice —————————————— KEY NS 3.3

Add or subtract.

1. $8.50 + $1.20

2. $6.23 − $1.08

3. $4.76 + $1.90

4. $0.46 + $1.32

Name _____ Date _____

Multiply a 3-Digit Number by a 1-Digit Number

CA Standards
KEY NS 2.4, MR 2.1

Find the product.

1. 214
× 2

2. 151
× 4

3. 419
× 2

4. 219
× 4

5. 217
× 3

6. 3 × 162 =

7. 2 × 448 =

8. 5 × 118 =

9. 3 × 316 =

Test Practice

10. Find the missing factor.

4 × _____ = 800

A 100   **C** 200

B 120   **D** 300

11. Find the missing factor.

3 × _____ = 750

A 150   **C** 250

B 200   **D** 300

12. Find the product.

362 × 2 =

A 564

B 624

C 634

D 724

Writing Math Marco wants to know the product of 3 × 112. Tell him how to find the product.

_____

_____

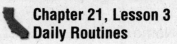
Regroup More Than Once

Problem of the Day ————————————————— KEY NS 2.4

In the first hour at the carnival, 142 ride tickets were sold. At this rate, how many tickets will be sold in the first 5 hours?

Number Sense Review ————————————————— KEY NS 2.2

There are 9 innings in a professional baseball game. How many total innings are there in 4 games? In 6 games?

Number of the Day ————————————————— NS 3.1

$\frac{3}{4}$

Use $\frac{3}{4}$ to describe some things in your classroom or school.

_____

_____

Facts Practice ————————————————— KEY NS 2.1

Find each difference.

1. 4,007 − 392

2. 730 − 125

3. 2,653 − 884

4. 3,266 − 1,804

Regroup More than Once

CA Standard
KEY NS 2.4

Multiply. Regroup if needed.

1. 105
   × 8

2. 198
   × 4

3. 619
   × 3

4. 728
   × 2

5. 1,191
   × 6

6. 2,268
   × 3

7. 4,321
   × 6

8. 3,546
   × 2

9. $7 \times 115 =$

10. $5 \times 313 =$

11. $4 \times 521 =$

12. $2 \times 579 =$

_____

_____

_____

_____

13. $5 \times 1,316 =$

14. $6 \times 1,141 =$

15. $4 \times 6,511 =$

16. $5 \times 3,310 =$

_____

_____

_____

_____

Test Practice

17. Jane's calculator shows 1,053. Which of these products did she multiply?

    A 5×333 C 5×355

    B 3×341 D 3×351

18. Mario traveled from his home to Los Angeles and back. Los Angeles is 1,237 miles from his home. How many miles did he travel in all?

    A 1,237   C 2,237

    B 2,474   D 2,484

Writing Math Can you regroup ones, tens, and hundreds in one multiplication problem? Give an example.

_____

Multiply Money

Problem of the Day ———————————————— KEY

A machine can make 375 baskets each hour. How many baskets
can the machine make in 6 hours?

Measurement Review ———————————————— KEY

Describe two different rectangles that have an area of 30
square units.

Number of the Day ———————————————— KEY NS 2.4

64

Show 64 as a product of three factors in three different ways.

_____

_____

_____

Facts Practice ———————————————— KEY

Find each product.

1. 4 × 200

2. 50 × 7

3. 8 × 300

4. 600 × 6

5. 9 × 80

Name _____ Date _____

Multiply Money

CA Standards
KEY NS 3.3, **KEY** NS 2.4

Find the product. Regroup if needed.

1. $1.25
   × 5

2. $3.24
   × 6

3. $1.75
   × 3

4. $4.49
   × 2

5. $5.79
   × 3

6. $1.99
   × 3

7. $4.26
   × 5

8. $2.72
   × 2

9. $3.15
   × 5

10. $3.10
    × 8

11. 6 × $5.41 =

12. 4 × $2.29 =

13. 9 × $1.19 =

14. 2 × $1.36 =

_____   _____   _____   _____

Test Practice

Circle the letter of the correct answer.

15. Find the product.

    4 × $2.39 =

    A $9.16

    B $9.17

    C $9.26

    D $9.56

16. If you bought 6 cans of vegetables for $0.65 each, how much would you spend?

    A more than $5.00

    B more than $4.00

    C less than $3.00

    D exactly $3.90

 Writing Math Max is multiplying 3 × $2.30. Tell him where to place the dollar sign and the decimal point in the product.

_____

_____

_____

Problem Solving: Make a Table

Problem of the Day KEY NS 3.3

Maya buys four chairs at $79 each. She pays with four $100 bills. What operations can you use to find how much change Maya should receive?

Number Sense Review KEY NS 3.3

Jon used 2 one-dollar bills, one quarter, two dimes, and two pennies to pay the cost of shipping a package. Marina used 1 one-dollar bill and three half-dollars to ship another package. Who paid more for shipping?

Word of the Day NS 3.0

model

How can you model a fraction? What other models have you used in math lessons?

_____

_____

_____

Facts Practice Grade 2 KEY NS 3.2

Find the quotient and remainder.

1. $50 \div 7$

2. $34 \div 5$

3. $42 \div 9$

4. $21 \div 4$

5. $36 \div 8$

Make a Table

CA Standards
MR 2.3, **KEY** AF 2.1

**Make a table to solve each problem. Explain why
your answer makes sense.**

1. Each classroom in Tracy's school has 18 desks. There are 8 classrooms in the school. How many desks are there in all of the classrooms together?

_____

2. On a field trip, each student collected exactly one dozen seashells. Nine students took part in the field trip. How many seashells did they collect in all?

_____

3. In the course of 1 hour, Patrick can read 14 pages. At this rate, how many pages can he read in 6 hours?

_____

Test Practice

Circle the letter of the correct answer.

4. Jan's parents gave her $12. Each week after that, they give her $5. How much money will Jan have at the end of four weeks?

   A $20   C $28

   B $32   D $36

5. For the first 45 minutes of the baseball game, every 22nd person in line gets in for free. In the first 45 minutes, 176 people arrive. How many people got in for free?

   A 7   C 8

   B 11   D 12

Writing Math In a table for problem #4, what number would you put in the first row of the "input" column? Explain.

_____

_____

_____

Hands On: Organize Data

Problem of the Day ———————————————— MR 2.3, KEY AF 2.1

Isabella had 12 different state quarters in her collection. Each month she got 4 more different state quarters. Make a table to help you find how many state quarters she had at the end of 6 months.

Number Sense Review ———————————————— NS 2.0

Tell whether each is *true* or *false*.

1. $23 \div 1 = 1$

2. $36 \times 1 = 36$

3. $0 \div 7 = 0$

4. $15 \times 0 = 15$

Number of the Day ———————————————— NS 1.1

25

Throughout the day, find ways to use the number 25. For example, you may have 25¢ or be 25th in line.

_____

_____

_____

Facts Practice ———————————————— KEY NS 2.1

Add.

1. $87 + 17$

2. $49 + 26$

3. $62 + 38$

4. $56 + 15$

5. $70 + 29$

6. $15 + 47$

Name _____ Date _____

Hands On: Organize Data

CA Standards
KEY SDAP 1.3, SDAP 1.4

Use the tally chart below for Problems 1–5.

Ways Students Get to School		
Way	**Tally**	**Number**
Walk	‖‖‖ ‖‖‖	8
Car	‖‖‖ ‖	6
Bus	‖‖‖ ‖‖‖ ‖‖‖	15
Bike	‖‖‖	3

1. How many students were surveyed?

_____

2. How many students ride in a car to get to school?

_____

3. Which way is used by the fewest number of students?

_____

4. Do more children walk or ride their bikes to school?

_____

5. If you added a tally mark for the way you get to school, how would the chart change?

_____

Test Practice

Circle the letter of the correct answer.

6. George surveyed 16 children. He wrote these tally marks on his chart: walk: ‖‖‖; car: ‖‖‖‖; bus: ‖‖‖ ‖‖; bike: ‖‖. How many children take the bus to school?

A 4   C 7

B 6   D 8

7. The results of a survey of 12 students were as follows: 1 walks to school, 2 ride in a car, 1 rides a bike, and the rest ride the bus. How many students ride the bus?

A 1   C 6

B 5   D 8

Writing Math Why is a tally chart a good way to record the answers to a survey?

_____

_____

Hands On: Pictographs

Problem of the Day ———————————————— KEY SDAP 1.3

Complete the survey table. Which grade has the most students on the bus?

Students Riding the School Bus

Grade	Tally	Number
1	IIII IIII II	
2	IIII II	
3	IIII IIII IIII I	

Algebra and Functions Review ———————— KEY AF 1.1

There are 4 runners on each relay team. Write a number sentence that shows how to find the number of runners on 6 relay teams.

Number of the Day ————————————————————— NS 1.1

12

How many eggs are in a dozen?

If you had 4 dozen eggs, how many eggs would you have?

_____

_____

_____

Facts Practice ——————————————————————— KEY NS 2.1

Add mentally.

1. 61 + 37   2. 99 + 21   3. 82 + 16

4. 84 + 61   5. 48 + 22   6. 35 + 45

Daily Routines and Practice

219

Use with Chapter 22, Lesson 2

Name _____   Date _____

Line Plots

The table below shows the number of catches that 6 players made in the last football game.

Player	Number of Catches
Brian	4
Peter	5
Joseph	5
Akiem	3
George	1
Patrick	0

1. Use the data to make a line plot. Then use your line plot to answer Questions 2 and 3.

2. How many players caught more than 3 passes?

_____

3. How many players caught fewer than 2 passes? _____

Test Practice

Use the line plot to answer problems 4–5. Circle the letter of the correct answer.

4. How many players made 2 tackles?

   A 1   C 3

   B 2   D 6

5. How many players made at least 3 tackles?

   A 3   C 6

   B 4   D 10

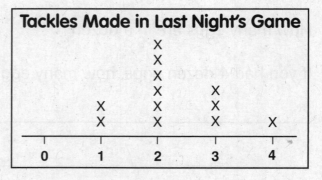

Tackles Made in Last Night's Game

Writing Math Is it easier to use the table or the line plot to answer Question 2? Explain.

_____

_____

_____

Hands On: Pictographs

Problem of the Day

Complete the survey table. Which grade has the most students on the bus?

Students Riding the School Bus

Grade	Tally	Number
1	IIII IIII II	12
2	IIII II	7
3	IIII IIII IIII I	16

Algebra and Functions Review

There are 4 runners on each relay team. Write a number sentence that shows how to find the number of runners on 6 relay teams.

Number of the Day

12

How many eggs are in a dozen?

If you had 4 dozen eggs, how many eggs would you have?

_____

_____

_____

Facts Practice

Add mentally.

1. $61 + 37$

2. $99 + 21$

3. $82 + 16$

4. $84 + 61$

5. $48 + 22$

6. $35 + 45$

Hands On: Pictographs

Use the pictograph to answer problems 1–4.

Favorite Field Day Events	
Balloon toss	👤 👤 👤 👤 👤 👤
Obstacle course	
100-yard dash	👤 👤 👤 👤 👤
Sack race	👤 👤 👤 👤 👤

Each 👤 stands for 2 votes.

1. The obstacle course had 9 votes. Show this on the pictograph.

_____

_____

2. Which event had the most votes?

_____

3. Which two events had the same number of votes?

_____

_____

4. How many votes were there in all?

_____

Test Practice

Circle the letter of the correct answer.

5. The key to a pictograph is: Each √ stands for 6 votes. How many √ stand for 30 votes?

A 4   C 6

B 5   D 8

6. The key to a pictograph is: Each √ stands for 4 votes. 5 √ stand for how many votes?

A 20   C 22

B $20\frac{1}{2}$ D 24

Writing Math You want to show 200 votes on a pictograph. What is a good number for each symbol to stand for? Why?

_____

_____

Hands On: Bar Graphs

Problem of the Day

Larry and Mori are doing a survey to find the types of pets owned by students at their school. The results are shown in this pictograph.

Pet Survey	
Dogs	🐱 🐱 🐱 🐱 🐱 🐱
Cats	🐱 🐱 🐱 🐱 🐱 🐱 🐱 🐱
Fish	🐱 🐱 🐱
Other	🐱 🐱

🐱 = 2 Pets

What is the total number of cats owned by students at Larry and Mori's school?

Geometry Review

Draw a parallelogram that is not a rectangle.

Word of the Day

Record

Give some examples of what you might record during the school day.

_____

_____

Facts Practice

Subtract.

1. $18 - 9$ 2. $17 - 8$ 3. $16 - 8$

4. $15 - 6$ 5. $14 - 8$ 6. $13 - 4$

Name _____ Date _____

Hands On: Bar Graphs

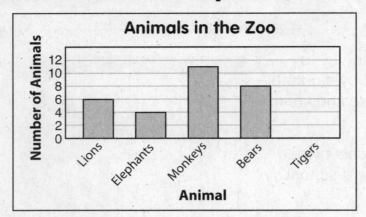

Use the bar graph to solve each problem.

1. There are 2 tigers in the zoo. Show that on the bar graph.

   _____

2. What is the scale of this graph?

   _____

3. How many lions are in the zoo?

   _____

4. Which animal is there the most of?

   _____

5. How many more monkeys are there than elephants?

   _____

6. The number of bears and tigers equals the number of what other two animals?

   _____

Test Practice

Use the bar graph above to solve and circle the letter of the correct answer.

7. When you add the numbers of these two animals in the zoo, the sum is the same as the number of bears.

   A elephants and tigers

   B lions and tigers

   C elephants and monkeys

   D elephants and lions

8. What is the total number of zoo animals?

   A 29   C 31

   B 30   D 32

 Writing Math What is one way a pictograph and a bar graph are alike?

Choose a Graph to Display Data

Problem of the Day ───────────── KEY SDAP 1.3

Bethany's team plays three games. In the first game they score 10 points, in the second, they score 15, and in the third they score 5. Use Workmat 8 to make a bar graph of the data.

Number Sense Review ───────────── NS 1.4

Round the numbers 68, 76, 57, and 51 to the nearest ten.

Number of the Day ───────────── NS 1.1

10

Throughout the day, find quantities that are about 10.

_____

_____

_____

Facts Practice ───────────── KEY NS 2.1

Add.

1. $3 + 5$

2. $4 + 7$

3. $9 + 5$

4. $8 + 6$

5. $10 + 5$

6. $5 + 8$

Choose a Graph to Display Data

Use the data from the tally chart to make a pictograph on a separate sheet of paper.

Use your pictograph to solve the problems.

1. What scale did you choose?

_____

2. How many symbols did you use to show pizza as the favorite?

_____

3. How many symbols did you use to show hamburger as the favorite?

_____

Favorite Lunch		
Lunch	Tally	Number
Pizza	‖‖‖ ‖‖‖ ‖‖‖ ‖‖‖ ‖‖‖ |||	28
Taco	‖‖‖ ‖‖‖ ‖‖‖ ‖‖‖	20
Hamburger	‖‖‖ ‖‖‖ ‖‖‖ |||	18
hot dog	‖‖‖ ‖‖‖ ‖‖‖		16

4. How many symbols would you use for tacos if 2 more students chose that lunch?

_____

Test Practice

Circle the letter of the correct answer.

5. A tally chart shows ‖‖‖ ‖‖‖ |||. What number does the tally show?

   A 11   c 13

   B 12   D 14

6. A bar on a bar graph is halfway between 6 and 10. What number does the bar show?

   A 6   c $7\frac{1}{2}$

   B 7   D 8

Writing Math You want to show how often players on a baseball team hit home runs. What is the best graph to use? Why?

_____

_____

Problem Solving: Use a Graph

Problem of the Day ———————————————— KEY SDAP 1.3

A bar graph has a scale of 0, 4, 8, 12, 16, …. Where would the
end of the bar representing the data number 10 be found?

Number Sense Review ———————————————— NS 1.4

Round each number to the nearest hundred.

1. 871

2. 404

3. 1,629

4. 4,782

Number of the Day ———————————————— KEY NS 2.1

7

What time is it 7 minutes from now?

_____

_____

_____

Facts Practice ———————————————— KEY NS 2.2

Multiply.

1. 6×3 2. 4×5 3. 7×6

4. 6×4 5. 5×2 6. 7×8

Name _____ Date _____

Use a Graph

Use the bar graph to solve each problem.

1. Who was the leading scorer for the Bears?

_____

2. What is the difference in points between the highest scorer and the lowest scorer for the Bears in the game against the Cougars? Explain.

_____

_____

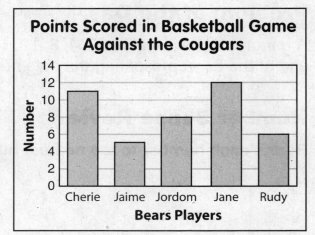

3. Cherie's brother promised her a candy bar for each 5 points she scored in the game against the Cougars. What will Cherie's brother give her?

_____

Test Practice

Circle the letter of the correct answer.

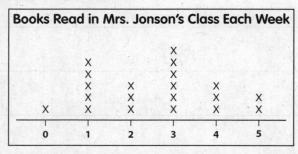

4. How many books were read during the period shown in the graph?

   A 6   c 20

   B 51   D 52

5. How many weeks does the graph illustrate?

   A 5   c 12

   B 20   D 52

 Writing Math How did you find the answer to problem #5?

Hands On: Record Outcomes

Problem of the Day ———————————————— MR 2.0

The graph shows how many boxes of tackle were sold. Mr. Zelda
said that on Wednesday he sold more boxes of tackle than on
Tuesday but fewer boxes of tackle than he sold on Monday.
Complete the graph.

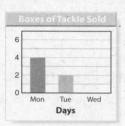

Algebra and Functions Review ———————————— AF 2.2

In a parking lot, there are spaces for 14 cars in one row. Two
rows have 28 spaces, and three rows have 42 spaces. If the rows
continue to have the same number of spaces, how many cars
can be parked in 4 rows?

Number of the Day ———————————————— KEY NS 2.4

36

Show 36 as a product of two factors in three different ways.

_____

_____

_____

Facts Practice ———————————————————— KEY NS 2.1

Add or subtract mentally.

1. 46 + 41   2. 68 − 32   3. 23 + 19

4. 75 − 52   5. 37 + 43   6. 84 − 29

Name _____   Date _____

Hands On: Record Outcomes

CA Standards
KEY SDAP 1.2, **KEY** SDAP

The tally chart shows the results of tossing a cube 20 times.
Complete the chart.

Color	Tally	Number
Purple	~~HHT~~ ~~HHT~~ II	
Green	~~HHT~~ III	

Use the tally chart to answer Problems 1–2.

1. What are the two possible
outcomes?

_____

2. What color are you least likely to
land on?

_____

Suppose you put these objects in a bag. Predict which object
you are more likely to pull out.

3.

4.

5.

6.

_____   _____   _____   _____

Test Practice

Circle the letter of the correct answer.

7. If Danny puts 7 green marbles, 2
pink marbles, and 12 blue marbles
in a box, which color marble is he
most likely to pull out?

   A green   **c** pink

   B blue   **D** yellow

8. Miriam is taking a coin out of a bag
of 50 pennies, 2 quarters, 10 nickels
and 25 dimes. Which coin is she
least likely to pick?

   A penny   **c** dime

   B nickel   **D** quarter

Writing Math Lilly placed 5 oranges, 1 peach, and 2
apples in a bag. Which fruit is she least likely to pull out of the
bag? Explain your reasoning.

Name _____ Date _____

Probability

Problem of the Day ——————————————— KEY SDAP 1.2

A spinner has 7 sections. Three sections are red, 2 are blue, and the rest are green. How many possible outcomes are there for each spin? Name them.

Number Sense Review ——————————————— KEY NS 3.2

Jon has 8 coins. Two of the coins are nickels. Three of the coins are dimes. Write a number sentence that shows the part of Jon's coins that are nickels or dimes.

Number of the Day ——————————————— NS 1.1

111

Write the other three-digit numbers made up of the same digit up to 999. For each three-digit number, find the sum of the digits. For example, $1 + 1 + 1 = 3$. What pattern do you see?

_____

_____

_____

Facts Practice ——————————————— NS 2.5

Divide.

1. $21 \div 7$ 2. $30 \div 6$ 3. $42 \div 7$

4. $28 \div 7$ 5. $54 \div 6$ 6. $70 \div 7$

Name _____ Date _____

Probability

CA Standard
SDAP 1.1

Chapter 23, Lesson 2
Practice

Write the word *certain, likely, unlikely,* or *impossible* to describe the probability of picking a smiley face.

1. ☺☺☺☺ 2. ☺○○○ 3. ○○○○ 4. ☺☺☺○

_____ _____ _____ _____

Write whether the event is *certain, likely, unlikely,* or *impossible.* Explain your answer.

5. There will be no Friday next week.

_____

_____

6. February 14th is Valentine's Day.

_____

_____

Draw a set of figures to represent each statement.

7. Picking a square is impossible.

_____

8. Picking a square is likely.

_____

_____

Test Practice

Circle the letter of the correct answer.

9. Read the sentence, then pick the correct answer.

Snow is made of frozen ice crystals that fall from the sky.

A certain C likely

B impossible D unlikely

10. What is the likehood that there will be no rain for the entire year?

A certain C likely

B impossible D unlikely

Writing Math John says, "It is likely that the sun will shine all week." Do you agree or disagree? Explain your answer.

_____

Daily Routines and Practice
Copyright © Houghton Mifflin Company. All rights reserved.

232

Use with text pp. 498–500

Hands On: Make Predictions

Problem of the Day

Ed put 5 red marbles and 2 blue marbles in a bag. He wants to add 1 marble to the bag to make it possible, but unlikely, to pick blue. What color marble should Ed add?

Statistics, Data Analysis, and Probability Review

A bag contains 5 pink tiles and 1 blue tile. Write whether each event is *certain, likely, unlikely,* or *impossible.*

1. pick a red tile

2. pick a blue tile

3. pick a pink tile

Number of the Day

463

Write 463 in expanded form and word form.

_____

_____

_____

Facts Practice

Find each product.

1. 12 × 3

2. 15 × 8

3. 19 × 6

4. 32 × 7

5. 24 × 5

6. 31 × 9

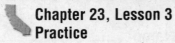
Hands On: Make Predictions

CA Standards
SDAP 1.4, KEY SDAP 1.3

Use the tables below to solve the following problems.

The following table shows the results of picking fruit out of a basket.

Type of Fruit	Number of Pieces
Apple	3
Pear	40
Oranges	12

1. How many more pears than oranges were taken out of the basket? _____

2. Which type of fruit is most likely to be picked next? _____

3. Which type of fruit is least likely to be picked next? _____

 **Test Practice**

Circle the letter of the correct answer.

4. Mara has a bag with 10 green marbles, 17 blue marbles, 5 yellow marbles, and 9 red marbles. If Mara picks a random marble from the bag, which color will she most likely pick?

   A green   C yellow

   B blue   D red

5. In a box of chocolates, there are 10 caramels, 2 nut candies, 4 fudge candies and 4 marshmallow candies. If Joey takes a candy from the box at random, which type will he most likely pick?

   A caramel   C fudge candy

   B nut candy   D marshmallow candy

Writing Math Janet flipped a coin and received 44 heads and 3 tails. Which would be a likely result for her next flip? Explain your answer.

_____

Make Predictions

Problem of the Day ——————————————— SDAP 1.0

There are 12 girls in Carla's class. There is the same number of boys. The name of each student in Carla's class is written on a card. The cards are placed in a bag, and one is picked without looking. Is it more likely that a girl's name or a boy's name is picked? Explain.

Measurement and Geometry Review ——————— KEY

Find the perimeter of this rectangle.

```
     8 cm
  ┌──────────┐
  │          │ 4 cm
  └──────────┘
```

Number of the Day ————————————————— AF 1.5

36

Complete each sentence.

$9 \times 4 = 36$, so $4 \times \underline{} = 36$

$(2 \times 3) \times 6 = 36$, so $2 \times (\underline{} \times 6) = 36$

Facts Practice ——————————————————— NS 1.4

Round each number to the nearest ten.

1. 83   **2.** 117   **3.** 294

4. 406   **5.** 197   **6.** 235

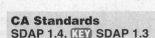
Make Predictions

CA Standards
SDAP 1.4, **KEY** SDAP 1.3

Use the graph to the right for Problems 1–2.

The graph shows the results of picking a bead from a bag 30 times. The bead was returned to the bag each time.

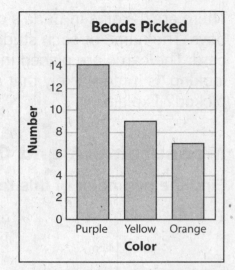

Beads Picked

1. Predict the color of the next bead to be picked.

   _____

2. Predict the color bead that will least likely be picked.

   _____

Solve.

3. Look at the tally table. Which coin do you predict will be picked next?

   _____

Picking Coins from a Bag

Outcome	Tally	Number
Penny	III	3
Dime	HHT II	7

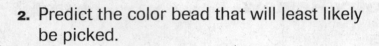

Test Practice

Circle the letter of the correct answer.

4. Brice has 20 color markers in a bag. Of the markers, 5 are red, 8 are blue, 3 are yellow, and 4 are orange. He reaches into the bag and pulls out a marker. What color do you predict the marker will be?

   A red   **c** blue

   B yellow   **D** orange

5. Rory selected 10 green marbles, 44 red marbles, 8 pink marbles and 12 yellow marbles. What do you predict will be the color of the next marble he chooses?

   A green   **c** pink

   B red   **D** yellow

Writing Math Alisa put 7 green tiles, 5 blue tiles, and 2 red tiles in a bag. Predict the color she is least likely to pull from the bag. Explain your reasoning.

Problem Solving: Field Trip

Problem of the Day ———————————————— SDAP 1.4

The tally chart shows the results of Carmen spinning a spinner 30 times. What color do you predict she will spin next?

Spinner Results

Outcome	Tally	Number
Red	IIII II	7
Blue	IIII IIII IIII	15
Yellow	IIII III	8

Measurement and Geometry Review ———————— KEY MG 2.2

Draw a right triangle.

Number of the Day ——————————————————— NS 1.0

2000

What could 2000 represent?

_____

_____

Facts Practice ———————————————————————— KEY NS 2.1

Subtract.

1. 82 − 75   2. 45 − 28   3. 51 − 37

4. 96 − 58   5. 60 − 34   6. 78 − 29

Hands On: Equal Groups

Problem of the Day

The table shows the high temperature forecast for the next three days. On which day are you most likely to wear a coat?

High Temperature Forecast

Day	High Temperature (°F)
Tuesday	60
Wednesday	70
Thursday	72

Number Sense Review

Write a 4-digit number that has a 2 in the thousands place and a 4 in the tens place.

Number of the Day

50

Throughout the day, find quantities that are about 50.

_____

_____

_____

Facts Practice

Add.

1. $52 + 48$ 2. $96 + 37$ 3. $48 + 85$

4. $37 + 79$ 5. $81 + 59$ 6. $79 + 74$

Name _____ Date _____

Hands On: Equal Groups

CA Standard
NS 2.0

Use counters to complete the table.

	Division	Number (dividend)	Number of Equal Groups (divisor)	Number in Each Group (quotient)	Number Left Over
1.	2)21				
2.	5)54				
3.	4)37				
4.	8)67				
5.	6)15				
6.	3)23				
7.	9)57				
8.	7)17				

Test Practice

Circle the letter of the correct answer.

9. Hillary had 51 postcards in her collection. She wanted to stack them into groups of 7. How many stacks did Hillary make? How many will be left over?

   A 6 with 3 left over

   B 7 with 2 left over

   C 10 with 1 left over

   D 8 with 3 left over

10. Morris split 23 granola bars equally for his 7 soccer buddies. How many granola bars did each friend receive? How many were left for Morris?

    A 10 with 3 left for Morris

    B 4 with 3 left for Morris

    C 7 with 2 left for Morris

    D 3 with 2 left for Morris

Writing Math Jan says that 42 ÷ 5 equals 7 with 7 left over. What did she do wrong?

_____

_____

Hands On: Repeated Subtraction

Problem of the Day ——————————————— NS 2.0

Five students are playing a math game with 36 cards. Each
student receives an equal number of cards to start the game.
What is the greatest number of cards each student can receive?
Will any cards be left over? If so, how many?

Algebra and Functions Review ———————————— AF 1.2

Write the numbers that make this sentence true.

$8 - 3 > \boxed{} - 4$

Number of the Day ——————————————— NS 2.0

8

What are some basic facts that have 8 as a sum, difference,
product, or quotient?

_____

_____

_____

Facts Practice ——————————————— KEY NS 2.2

Multiply.

1. 3×7 2. 9×6 3. 5×8

4. 4×7 5. 8×6 6. 9×9

Hands On: Repeated Subtraction
CA Standard
NS 2.0

Use counters and repeated subtraction to complete the table.

	Division	Number (dividend)	Number of Equal Groups (divisor)	Number in Each Group (quotient)	Number Left Over
1.	7)55				
2.	2)21				
3.	5)19				
4.	9)33				
5.	4)22				
6.	3)32				
7.	4)31				
8.	6)53				

Test Practice

Circle the letter of the correct answer.

9. Danni split his collection of 70 toy cars among his 8 cousins. How many toy cars did each cousin receive? How many were left over?

   A 6 with 0 left over

   B 8 with 6 left over

   c 7 with 5 left over

   D 10 with 4 left over

10. Estella's mother bought 32 party favors for Estella's birthday party. Nine of Estella's friends were to attend. How many party favors did each friend receive? How many were left over?

    A 5 with 2 left

    B 10 with 2 left

    c 3 with 5 left

    D 8 with 0 left

Writing Math What is the greatest number that can be left over in a division problem?

Use Multiples

Problem of the Day ———————————————— NS 2.0

There are 50 students in the school choir. For a concert, they will stand in as many full rows of 9 as possible. Use repeated subtraction to find how many students will not be in a full row.

Measurement and Geometry Review ———————— MG 2.5

Name or draw an object that looks like a cylinder.

Word of the Day ——————————————————— MR 2.3

complete

What are some things that you may complete during a school day?

_____

_____

_____

Facts Practice ——————————————————— NS 1.4

Round to the nearest hundred.

1. 238   **2.** 467   **3.** 724

4. 390   **5.** 154   **6.** 986

Name _____ Date _____

Use Multiples

CA Standard
KEY NS 2.3

Complete the table.

	Division	What multiplication fact can you use?	Number in Each Group (quotient)	Number Left Over
1.	4)27			
2.	2)9			
3.	7)55			
4.	5)43			
5.	7)32			
6.	9)44			
7.	3)26			
8.	8)19			

Test Practice

Circle the letter of the correct answer.

9. Roni's father planted 29 olive trees in rows. Each row had 7 olive trees. Which multiplication fact best represents the situation?

   A $2 \times 7 = 14$ with 19 left over   C $4 \times 7 = 28$ with 1 left over

   B $3 \times 7 = 21$ with 8 left over   D $5 \times 7 = 35$ with 0 left over

10. Elise had 44 sheets of construction paper to divide equally among 5 group members. Which multiplication fact best represents the situation?

   A $5 \times 8 = 40$ with 4 left over   C $3 \times 8 = 24$ with 20 left over

   B $4 \times 8 = 32$ with 12 left over   D $6 \times 8 = 48$ with 0 left over

Writing Math Look at problems 1–8. Which number in the division problem do you use in the multiplication fact?

Problem Solving: Total Cost and Unit Cost

Problem of the Day ———————————————————————————— KEY NS 2.3

A bakery sells bagels in bags of 6 and individually. It has
38 bagels left to sell. If it sells as many full bags as possible,
how many bagels can it sell individually? Explain.

Statistics, Data Analysis and Probability Review —— SDAP 1.1

**Name an event that is possible but unlikely to happen at
school today.**

Number of the Day ———————————————————————————————— NS 3.4

$\frac{1}{2}$

What are some ways that you can make $\frac{1}{2}$ of a dollar?

_____

_____

_____

Facts Practice ————————————————————————————————— KEY NS 2.1

Subtract mentally.

  1. 85 − 20   **2.** 97 − 47   **3.** 65 − 34

  4. 43 − 29   **5.** 50 − 31   **6.** 70 − 42

Total Cost and Unit Cost

CA Standards
MR 2.4, NS 2.7

Solve. Explain why your answer makes sense.

1. Philip bought 5 posters to decorate a room in his house. All the posters were the same price. The total cost was $40. How much money did each poster cost? _____

2. The total cost for 4 sandwiches is $20. Each sandwich is the same price. What is the unit cost? _____

3. One wall map of the world costs $6. Two wall maps of the world cost $12. Three wall maps of the world cost $18. If the cost increase remains the same, how much would 5 wall maps of the world cost? _____

4. Ingrid's mother bought 7 party favors for the 7 friends who were invited to Ingrid's birthday party. All the party favors were the same price. The total cost was $21. How much did each party favor cost? _____

5. The total cost for 6 CDs is $48. Each CD is the same price. What is the unit cost? _____

6. One rug costs $13. Two rugs cost $26. Three rugs cost $39. If the cost increase remains the same, how much would 4 rugs cost? _____

Test Practice

Circle the letter of the correct answer.

7. The total cost for 4 books is $28. Each book is the same price. What is the unit cost?

   A $4   c $7

   B $28   D $112

8. The total cost for 7 greeting cards is $21. Each greeting card is the same price. What is the price of 5 greeting cards?

   A $3   c $7

   B $15   D $21

Writing Math Explain the steps you used to solve problem #8.

_____

_____

_____

Hands On: Divide 2-Digit Numbers

Problem of the Day ————————————————— NS 2.7

A runner paid $20 for 5 energy bars. Each energy bar is the
same price. How much would the runner have to pay for
3 energy bars?

Number Sense Review ————————————————— NS 1.2

Write these numbers in order from least to greatest:
253, 532, 235, 325.

Number of the Day ————————————————— NS 1.1

48

What are some ways you can show 48?

_____

_____

_____

Facts Practice ————————————————— NS 2.5

Divide.

1. $64 \div 8$ 2. $54 \div 9$ 3. $72 \div 9$

4. $32 \div 8$ 5. $40 \div 8$ 6. $81 \div 9$

Hands On: Divide 2-Digit Numbers

CA Standard
NS 2.5

Use base-ten blocks to help you divide.

1. 5)55 _____   2. 8)48 _____

3. 3)81 _____   4. 2)68 _____

5. 7)28 _____   6. 9)90 _____

7. 8)88 _____   8. 7)77 _____

9. 3)96 _____   10. 4)84 _____

Test Practice

Circle the letter of the correct answer.

11. Which is 44 divided by 11?

  A 4   c 33

  B 8   D 55

12. Max put a total of 24 pairs of socks into 3 drawers. If he put an equal number of pairs in each drawer, how many pairs of socks does he put in each drawer?

  A 3   c 6

  B 8   D 12

 Writing Math Elizabeth's group must do a 45-question assignment. If there are 5 students in the group, and each student answers the same number of questions, how many questions must each student answer? How do you know?

Hands On: Regroup in Division

Problem of the Day ———————————————— NS 2.5

Sixty-three runners signed up for training to run a marathon.
They are divided into 3 equal groups. Use base-ten blocks to find
how many runners are in each group.

Algebra and Functions Review ——————————— KEY AF 1.1

Tyler trains by riding his bicycle 25 miles each day. Today he got
a flat tire after riding 18 miles. Write a number sentence that
shows how many miles Tyler has left to ride after he repairs
the tire.

Word of the Day ———————————————————— MR 2.4

check

What are some things you check during a day?

_____

_____

_____

Facts Practice ——————————————————————— KEY NS 2.4

Multiply.

1. 24×6 2. 65×2 3. 37×4

4. 46×9 5. 19×3 6. 53×7

Name _____ Date _____

Hands On: Regroup in Division

Use base-ten blocks to help you divide.

1. 3)12 _____

2. 4)64 _____

3. 3)70 _____

4. 6)77 _____

5. 7)84 _____

6. 8)92 _____

7. 9)35 _____

8. 7)79 _____

9. 3)25 _____

10. 6)88 _____

 **Test Practice**

Circle the letter of the correct answer.

11. Which is 52 divided by 6?

    A 48   C 8 R4

    B 9   D 9 R2

12. Mimi made 48 cupcakes. If she divides them evenly among her 4 friends, how many cupcakes does she give to each friend?

    A 4   C 12

    B 44   D 52

Writing Math Benny is using base-ten blocks to model 57 divided by 3. He divided the tens into equal groups. He converted the remaining 10's into 20 ones. Then he divided 20 by 3, and put the ones into equal groups of 6, with 2 leftover. What did he forget to do?

_____

_____

Divide 2-Digit Numbers

Problem of the Day ———————————————— NS 2.7

Marla and her 4 friends paid $85 for basketball game tickets.
Each ticket cost the same amount. Use base-ten blocks to find
how much each ticket cost.

Measurement and Geometry Review ————————— MG 1.4

Write the number of minutes in 2 hours.

Number of the Day ————————————— KEY NS 1.3

78

What are some different ways you can show 78 as tens
and ones?

_____

_____

_____

Facts Practice ——————————————————— NS 1.4

Round each to the nearest thousand.

1. 7,702   2. 3,140   3. 2,978

4. 8,500   5. 5,425   6. 4,083

Name _____ Date _____

Divide 2-Digit Numbers

CA Standard
NS 2.5, **KEY** NS 2.3

Use base-ten blocks to help you divide.

1. $3\overline{)66}$ 2. $7\overline{)74}$ 3. $3\overline{)65}$ 4. $4\overline{)86}$ 5. $2\overline{)62}$

6. $3\overline{)97}$ 7. $2\overline{)26}$ 8. $4\overline{)47}$ 9. $3\overline{)99}$ 10. $2\overline{)43}$

11. $92 \div 3$ 12. $68 \div 6$ 13. $83 \div 2$ 14. $69 \div 2$

_____   _____   _____   _____

Algebra • Symbols   Use >, <, or = for each ◯.

15. $48 \div 2$ ◯ 20   16. $48 \div 4$ ◯ 12   17. $200 \div 5$ ◯ 50

18. 13 ◯ $88 \div 4$ 19. 14 ◯ $22 \div 2$ 20. $240 \div 6$ ◯ 40

21. 12 ◯ $63 \div 3$ 22. 50 ◯ $320 \div 8$ 23. $100 \div 5$ ◯ 10

Test Practice

Circle the letter of the correct answer.

24. What is 55 divided by 5?

A 9

B 10

C 11

D 12

25. Diana has 46 pieces of candy to give to her 4 cousins. If she gives each cousin an equal number of pieces, how many pieces of candy will she have left over?

A 0   C 2

B 1   D 3

 Writing Math Drew wants to put 69 paper clips into 3 boxes. He wants the same number of paper clips in each box. How many paper clips should he put in each box? Explain how you found your answer.

Problem Solving: Field Trip

Problem of the Day ————————————

A swim team had displayed all the medals it had won in its
history in 4 rows. Each row contained 18 medals. Now the
medals are displayed in 3 equal rows. How many medals are in
each row?

Statistics, Data Analysis, and Probability Review

The sides of a number cube are labeled with the first six
multiples of 2. The cube is tossed once. Name all the possible
outcomes.

Number of the Day ————————————

30

What are some things about time that can be described with 30?

_____

_____

Facts Practice ————————————

Multiply.

1. 7×7 2. 4×6 3. 9×3

4. 8×7 5. 5×9 6. 3×8

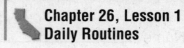
Hands On: Divide 3-Digit Numbers

Problem of the Day ——————————————————— NS 3.0

Theo wants to print 87 digital photos. He printed one-third of the photos before he ran out of paper. How many photos does Theo have left to print?

Number Sense Review ——————————————— KEY **NS 1.5**

Write 3,248 in expanded form.

_____

Number of the Day ——————————————————— NS 1.0

254

What are some ways you can show 254?

_____

_____

Facts Practice ——————————————————————— NS 2.5

Divide.

1. $35 \div 7$ 2. $45 \div 5$ 3. $54 \div 9$

4. $24 \div 4$ 5. $48 \div 6$ 6. $56 \div 8$

Name _____ Date _____

Hands On: Divide 3-Digit Numbers

CA Standards
NS 2.5, MR 2.3

Use base-ten blocks to help you divide.

1. 5)555

2. 8)488

3. 3)810

4. 2)684

5. 7)287

6. 9)909

7. 8)883

8. 7)774

9. 3)962

10. 4)845

 **Test Practice**

Circle the letter of the correct answer.

11. Willa used 585 airtime minutes in 5 weeks. How many airtime minutes did she use per week?

   A 107 minutes   C 111 minutes

   B 117 minutes   D 590 minutes

12. Divide 4)864.

   A 208   C 210 R2

   B 216   D 860

Writing Math Evan drove into the country for a long weekend. He planned to drive 118 miles on each of 4 days, however his car broke down and he was only able to drive 43 miles on the first day. How many miles per day must he drive to reach his destination? Explain how you know.

_____

_____

_____

Divide 3- and 4-Digit Numbers

Problem of the Day

KEY NS 2.4

In the spring, a city bought small trees to plant in its parks. The trees were divided equally, and 115 trees were planted in each of 5 parks. How many trees did the city plant in all?

Measurement and Geometry Review

KEY MG 1.2

Find the area of the rectangle.

```
    4 units
  ┌─────────┐
  │         │ 2 units
  └─────────┘
```

Number of the Day

NS 1.1

100

Name some things that have special names when there are 100 of them.

_____

_____

_____

Facts Practice

KEY NS 2.1

Add.

1. 48 + 47   2. 56 + 63   3. 92 + 18

4. 17 + 85   5. 88 + 74   6. 23 + 89

Divide 3- and 4-Digit Numbers

CA Standards
NS 2.5, MR 2.2

Divide and check.

1. $2\overline{)238}$

2. $6\overline{)696}$

3. $4\overline{)478}$

4. $4\overline{)466}$

5. $5\overline{)560}$

6. $3\overline{)672}$

7. $3\overline{)681}$

8. $4\overline{)853}$

9. $2\overline{)628}$

10. $3\overline{)948}$

11. $422 \div 2$

12. $595 \div 5$

13. $876 \div 4$

14. $598 \div 5$

_____ _____ _____ _____

15. $654 \div 3$

16. $528 \div 3$

17. $872 \div 4$

18. $477 \div 2$

_____ _____ _____ _____

Test Practice

Circle the letter of the correct answer.

19. What is 856 divided by 4?

   A 223   C 214

   B 225   D 242

20. What is 384 divided by 3?

   A 128   C 129

   B 130   D 131

Writing Math Find the quotient. Explain how you found your answer.

$957 \div 3 =$ _____

Divide Money

Problem of the Day ———————————————— NS 2.5

A farmer brought 768 apples to the Fall Festival. He sold one basket of 24 apples. He put the rest of the apples in bags of 6 to sell. How many bags did he fill with apples?

Number Sense Review ———————————————— NS 1.1

Write the largest 4-digit number possible using zero and three different nonzero digits.

_____

Number of the Day ———————————————— NS 1.1

5

Count by the number of cents in a nickel to 100.

_____

_____

Facts Practice ———————————————— KEY

Subtract.

1. 56 − 41   2. 74 − 38   3. 49 − 23

4. 85 − 17   5. 90 − 57   6. 31 − 24

Divide Money

CA Standards
KEY NS 3.3, NS 2.7

Divide. Model with coins and bills if you wish.

1. 3)$3.75   2. 4)$4.88   3. 3)$9.78   4. 2)$6.42

5. $5.96 ÷ 2   6. $8.44 ÷ 2   7. $7.14 ÷ 2   8. $6.96 ÷ 6

_____   _____   _____   _____

Complete each table. If the rule is not given, write the rule.

Rule: Divide by 4	
Input	Output
$8.00	$2.00
9. $9.00	
10. $1.24	
11.	$3.00

	Rule: Divide by 3	
	Input	Output
12.	$9.36	
13.		$2.11
14.		$1.14
15.	$1.32	

16.	Rule: _____	
	Input	Output
	$4.22	$2.11
	$6.42	$3.21
17.	$1.20	
18.	$5.24	

Test Practice

Circle the letter of the correct answers.

19. $6.33 ÷ 3 = _____

   A $1.22   c $2.21

   B $2.11   D $2.22

20. Jerry spent $3.25 on 5 packs of candy. What is the price per pack?

   A $0.60   c $0.65

   B $0.70   D $0.75

 Writing Math Kay bought 4 notebooks for $8.64. What was the cost of 1 notebook? Explain.

_____

Place the First Digit

Problem of the Day ——————————————————— NS 2.7

One bookstore sells 2 puzzle books for $5.80. Another bookstore
sells 3 puzzle books for $8.55. Which puzzle books have the
lower unit cost?

Statistics, Data Analysis, and Probability Review · KEY SDAP 1.3

Jason surveyed his friends about how many jigsaw puzzles they
have ever done. The results are shown in this line plot.

```
Jigsaw Puzzles
Completed
            X
            X
    X       X
    X   X   X       X
    X   X   X   X   X   X
    0   1   2   3   4   5
```

How many jigsaw puzzles have most of Jason's friends
completed?

Number of the Day ——————————————————— NS 1.1

138

One hundred thirty-eight could be the number of what things
or people?

_____

_____

_____

Facts Practice ——————————————————————— NS 1.4

Round to the nearest hundred.

1. 2,462

2. 7,830

3. 1,753

4. 5,342

5. 3,998

6. 8,671

Place the First Digit

CA Standards
NS 2.5, **KEY** NS 2.3

Divide. Check your answers.

1. 5)195   2. 2)188   3. 4)348   4. 2)132   5. 3)123

6. 284 ÷ 4   7. 146 ÷ 2   8. 105 ÷ 5   9. 432 ÷ 8

_____   _____   _____   _____

Algebra • Equations Solve for _n_.

10. 848 ÷ 2 = _n_   11. 48 ÷ 2 = _n_   12. 536 ÷ 2 = _n_   13. 864 ÷ 2 = _n_

    848 ÷ 4 = _n_   48 ÷ 4 = _n_   536 ÷ 4 = _n_   864 ÷ 4 = _n_

    848 ÷ 8 = _n_   48 ÷ 8 = _n_   536 ÷ 8 = _n_   864 ÷ 8 = _n_

_____   _____   _____   _____

_____   _____   _____   _____

_____   _____   _____   _____

Test Practice

Circle the letter of the correct answers.

14. Find 792 ÷ 8.   15. Find _n_: 548 ÷ _n_ = 137.

    A 89   C 98   A 3   C 4

    B 97   D 99   B 5   D 6

Writing Math A meeting room has 150 seats. There are
5 rows. How many seats are in each row? Explain how you found
your answer.

_____

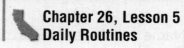
Problem Solving: Multistep Problems

Problem of the Day ————————————————— NS 2.5

A gardener has 125 tulip bulbs to plant 4 inches apart in 5 equal rows. How many bulbs should he plant in each row?

Algebra and Functions Review ————————— AF 1.3

Write an equation to show that 2 times a number is equal to 9 plus 3.

Word of the Day ————————————————————— MR 2.3

list

What are some lists that you or your family make?

_____

_____

_____

Facts Practice ————————————————————— KEY NS 2.2

Multiply.

1. 3×8 2. 7×4 3. 6×3

4. 5×7 5. 8×9 6. 9×7

Name _____ Date _____

Problem Solving: Multistep Problems

Solve.

1. The sewing club made a quilt to celebrate Earth Day. The quilt has 6 rows of 5 equal squares. Lydia made $\frac{1}{3}$ of the quilt squares. How many quilt squares did Lydia make?

2. Donny had 5 packs each of red, white, blue, and black buttons in his sewing room. Each pack had 2 buttons. He used $\frac{1}{8}$ of the buttons to make his costume for the school play. How many buttons did he use?

 **Test Practice**

Circle the letter of the correct answers.

3. Mary has 30 oranges. She gave half of the oranges to her brother, and divided the remaining oranges evenly among her three sisters. How many oranges did she give to each of her sisters?

   A 5   c 6

   B 10   D 15

4. Xiawu wants to read 416 pages of a book in 5 days. If he read $\frac{1}{4}$ of the book on the first day, how many pages does he need to read on each of the four days afterwards?

   A 78   c 83

   B 104   D 111

Writing Math Maxine ate $\frac{1}{8}$ of a pie. If she splits the remainder of the pie evenly among her 8 friends, will each piece be larger, smaller or the same size as the piece she already ate? How do you know?

_____

_____

Hands On: Estimate and Measure Capacity

Problem of the Day ——— NS 2.7, NS 2.8

At the end of the summer, one store has T-shirts on sale at 3 for $16.50. If Jeremy buys 2 T-shirts, how much will he pay?

Measurement and Geometry Review ——— MG 1.1

A worm is 5 units long. Tell whether those units are inches, feet, or yards.

Word of the Day ——— MR 1.1

pattern

Describe some patterns you find in the classroom.

_____

_____

_____

Facts Practice ——— NS 2.5

Divide.

1. $21 \div 7 =$ 2. $42 \div 7 =$ 3. $14 \div 7 =$

4. $77 \div 7 =$ 5. $63 \div 7 =$ 6. $49 \div 7 =$

Name _____ Date _____

Hands On: Estimate and Measure Capacity

CA Standards
MG 1.1, MG 1.4

Find the missing amount. Use the chart for help.

1 pint (pt) = 2 cups (c)
1 quart (qt) = 2 pints
1 gallon (gal) = 4 quarts

1. 4 qt = _____ pt

2. 4 pt = _____ c

3. 4 gal = _____ qt

4. 5 qt = _____ pt

5. 6 gal = _____ qt

6. 1 gal = _____ pt

7. 1 qt = _____ c

8. 3 pt = _____ c

9. 2 qt = _____ c

10. 3 gal = _____ pt

11. 2 gal = _____ pt

12. 2 qt = _____ pt

13. 4 qt = _____ c

Test Practice

Circle the letter of the correct answer.

14. How many quarts are in 5 gallons?

   A 10   **C** 20

   B 30   **D** 40

15. How many quarts are in 16 pints?

   A 2   **C** 6

   B 4   **D** 8

Writing Math Ben says that he multiplied twice to find the number of cups in 3 quarts. Describe the steps that he used.

_____

_____

Customary Units of Capacity

Problem of the Day ——————————————— MG 1.1, MG 1.4

Mui-Lin is making punch. The recipe calls for 5 cups of orange juice, 4 cups of cranberry juice, and 3 cups of grape juice. Which size container should she use to hold all of the punch—cup, gallon, pint, or quart?

Statistics, Data Analysis, and Probability Review — KEY **SDAP 1.3**

Use the bar graph to answer the questions below.

1. How many people named basketball as their favorite team sport?

2. Which two team sports were named by the same number of people?

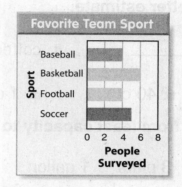

Number of the Day ——————————————— NS 1.4

3,528

Round 3,528 to the nearest thousand, the nearest hundred, and the nearest ten.

_____

_____

_____

Facts Practice ——————————————— KEY **NS 2.4**

Multiply.

1. 89 × 2   2. 66 × 8   3. 34 × 3

4. 13 × 5   5. 21 × 7   6. 47 × 6

Name _____ Date _____

Customary Units of Capacity

CA Standards
MG 1.1, MG 1.0

Choose the best unit to use for the container.
Write *cup*, *pint*, *quart*, or *gallon*.

1. 4 quarts

2. 2 cups

3. 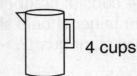 4 cups

_____ _____ _____

Choose the better estimate.

4. bath tub _____

    a. 40 gal   **b.** 40 c

5. coffee mug _____

    a. 1 qt   **b.** 1 c

6. bucket _____

    a. 3 c   **b.** 3 qt

Write in order from least capacity to greatest capacity.

7. 2 quarts   3 pints   1 gallon

8. 1 pint   1 quart   3 cups

_____ _____

Test Practice

Circle the letter of the correct answer.

9. Which is equal to 6 cups?

    A 1 gallon   **C** 2 quarts

    B 2 pints   **D** 3 pints

10. Which measure is equal to 4 gallons?

    A 16 cups   **C** 16 quarts

    B 32 cups   **D** 32 quarts

Writing Math Which unit would you use to measure the capacity of a swimming pool: cups or gallons? Explain.

_____

_____

Hands On: Estimate and Measure Weight

Problem of the Day ———————————————— MG 1.1, MG 1.0

Which is the best estimate for the capacity of a kitchen sink:
10 cups, 10 pints, 10 quarts, 10 gallons?

Number Sense Review ———————————————— NS 3.4

Write a fraction to tell what part of a dollar each amount of
money is.

1. 25 cents

2. 50 cents

3. 75 cents

Word of the Day ———————————————— MR 2.3

reasonable

What are some reasonable numbers that describe the school?

_____

_____

_____

Facts Practice ———————————————— KEY NS 2.1

Subtract mentally.

1. 47 − 27   2. 58 − 30   3. 65 − 5

4. 34 − 21   5. 82 − 38   6. 75 − 49

Hands On: Estimate and Measure Weight

CA Standards
MG 1.1, MG 1.0

Estimate the weight of each object. Write _more_ or _less_ than 1 pound.

1.

_____

2.

_____

3.

_____

4.

_____

5.

_____

6.

_____

7.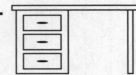

_____

8.

_____

Test Practice

Circle the letter of the correct answer.

9. Choose the best estimate for the weight of a table.

   A 1 ounce   C 1 pound

   B 50 ounces   D 50 pounds

10. Choose the best estimate for the weight of a bumblebee.

   A 1 ounce   C 1 pound

   B 8 ounces   D 8 pounds

Writing Math Lori purchased a bag of 20 tomatoes.
What would be a good estimate for the weight of the bag?
Explain how you know.

_____

Customary Units of Weights

Problem of the Day ——————————— MG 1.1, MG 1.4

Tony wanted to buy 1 pound of nuts. He bought 5 ounces of peanuts, 3 ounces of cashews, and 7 ounces of pecans. Did Tony buy 1 pound of nuts? Explain.

Measurement and Geometry Review ——————— MG 2.4

Draw a triangle that has an angle greater than a right angle.

Number of the Day ——————————————— NS 1.0

2,303

What are some ways you can show 2,303?

_____

_____

_____

Facts Practice ————————————————— KEY NS 2.1

Add mentally.

1. 23 + 23   **2.** 48 + 50   **3.** 43 + 37

4. 59 + 32   **5.** 64 + 29   **6.** 35 + 48

Customary Units of Weight

**Choose the unit you would use to measure the weight.
Write *ounce* or *pound*.**

1.

2.

3.

_____

4. an apple

5. a car

6. a sock

_____   _____   _____

Write in order from the least weight to the greatest weight.

7. 25 oz   15 oz   1 lb

8. 35 oz   2 lb   30 oz

_____   _____

 **Test Practice**

Circle the letter of the correct answer.

9. Choose the best estimate of the weight of a feather.

   A 1 ounce   C 100 pounds

   B 10 pounds   D 100 ounces

10. Which is equal to 4 pounds?

    A 48 ounces   C 64 ounces

    B 72 ounces   D 98 ounces

 Writing Math How many ounces are equal to 2 pounds? Explain how you know.

_____

_____

Convert Customary Units and Units of Time

Problem of the Day ——————————————— MG 1.1, MG 1.0

Which is the best estimate for the weight of a toaster:
5 oz, 15 oz, 5 lb, 50 lb?

Algebra and Functions Review ————————— KEY AF 1.1

James gave away 9 baseball cards to each of 12 friends. Write
a number sentence that shows how to find how many baseball
cards James gave away in all.

Number of the Day ——————————————————— NS 3.1

$\frac{1}{2}$

Name two fractions that are equivalent to $\frac{1}{2}$. Draw pictures if you need help.

_____

_____

_____

Facts Practice ————————————————————— KEY NS 2.2

Multiply.

1. 9×3 2. 2×6 3. 8×7

4. 7×4 5. 4×8 6. 6×7

Convert Customary Units and Units of Time

Choose the expression you would use to convert the units.
Then write the product or quotient.

1. number of pints in 4 quarts

_____

_____

2. number of inches in 10 feet

_____

_____

3. number of feet in 15 yards

_____

_____

4. number of yards in 108 inches

_____

_____

5. number of quarts in 10 gallons

_____

_____

6. number of pints in 44 cups

_____

_____

7. number of yards in 30 feet

_____

_____

8. number of gallons in 36 quarts

_____

_____

Test Practice

Circle the letter of the correct answer.

9. Which is equal to 18 feet?

  A 3 yards   c 4 yards

  B 5 yards   D 6 yards

10. Which is equal to 3 pints?

  A 6 cups   c 8 cups

  B 10 cups   D 12 cups

Writing Math Billy is baking a pie and needs to use 4 cups of flour. Dan tells him he can use 2 pints instead. Is Dan correct? Explain.

_____

_____

Problem Solving: Unit Costs

Problem of the Day ———————————————— AF 1.4, MG 1.4

Marcella is 4 feet tall. Write an expression that you can use to find Marcella's height in inches. Then find her height in inches.

Statistics, Data Analysis, and Probability Review — KEY SDAP 1.3

Use the data below to make a pictograph. Be sure to include a key.

Favorite Snacks	
Snack	**Number of Students**
Popcorn	12
Grapes	14
Apple	8
Granola	10

Number of the Day ———————————————————— NS 1.0

60

Name some things that 60 can represent.

_____

_____

_____

Facts Practice ———————————————————————— NS 1.4

Round each to the nearest ten.

1. 238

2. 576

3. 712

4. 845

5. 404

6. 653

Unit Costs

CA Standards
MR 2.4, NS 2.7

Solve. Explain why your answer makes sense.

1. A 30-ounce bunch of bananas costs $3.30. A 2-pound bag of California Bing cherries costs $5.44. Write a number sentence that shows the relationship between the unit prices of these two fruits.

_____

2. One package of dental floss contains 100 feet of floss and costs $4. Another package of dental floss contains 225 feet of dental floss and costs $4.50. What is the unit price of each package of dental floss?

_____

_____

3. A package of 8 postcards costs $6.80. Individual postcards are available for $0.95. Is it cheaper to buy the package or 8 individual postcards?

_____

_____

Test Practice

Circle the letter of the correct answer.

4. A 1-pound bag of Brand X flour costs $0.96. Brand Y flour is on sale for $0.05 per ounce. What is the difference in unit price between Brand X and Brand Y?

  A $0.01   c $0.11

  B $0.06   D $0.14

5. A quart of apple juice sells for $1.19. A gallon of apple juice sells for $3.80. Which of the following expresses the difference in unit price between the quart and the gallon size?

  A $4.76 < $7.60   c $2.38 > $0.95

  B $3.57 < $3.80   D $1.19 > $0.95

Writing Math Explain how you converted units to solve problem #5.

Hands On: Metric Units of Capacity

Problem of the Day ———————————— NS 2.7, NS 2.8

Which costs less per unit: 1 yard of ribbon for $2.40 or 5 feet of ribbon for $4.10? Explain your answer.

Measurement and Geometry Review ———————— MG 1.1

A pencil is 15 units long. Tell whether those units are centimeters or millimeters.

Number of the Day ———————————————— NS 1.2

987

What other numbers can you write with the same digits as the number 987 has? Write the numbers in order from least to greatest.

_____

_____

_____

Facts Practice ——————————————————— KEY NS 2.1

Add.

1. 52 + 37   **2.** 45 + 89   **3.** 67 + 54

4. 19 + 98   **5.** 84 + 66   **6.** 36 + 36

Hands On: Metric Units of Capacity

CA Standard
MG 1.1

Choose the better estimate for the capacity of each.

1.

2 L or 20 mL

_____

2.

300 L or 300 mL

_____

3.

8 L or 80 L

_____

Choose the unit you would use to measure the capacity of each. Write *mL* or *L*.

4. a sink

_____

5. a container of eye drops

_____

6. a washing machine

_____

7. a toothpaste tube

_____

8. a measuring spoon

_____

9. a pitcher

_____

Test Practice

Circle the letter of the correct answer.

10. Which of the following would you measure using milliliters (mL)?

   A a sink

   B a pail of water

   C a pool

   D a bottle cap

11. Which of the following would you measure using liters (L)?

   A cup of yogurt

   B spoon

   C pool

   D bottle of perfume

Writing Math If one sink can hold 4,500 mL of water and another can hold 4 L of water, which sink has the greater capacity? Explain.

_____

_____

Hands On: Metric Units of Mass

Problem of the Day —————————————— MG 1.1

Karen needs 750 milliliters of water. She has a jar with 600 mL.
She also has a 1-liter bottle of water. Karen pours water from the
bottle into the jar to make 750 milliliters. How many milliliters of
water will be left in the 1-liter bottle?

Algebra and Functions Review ————————— KEY **AF 2.1**

There are seats for 12 students at one cafeteria table. There are
seats for 24 students at two cafeteria tables. If each table has the
same number of seats, how many students can sit at five tables?

Word of the Day ————————————————— MR 2.1

better estimate

Throughout the day, offer two estimates for a situation, such as
the number of students in the cafeteria during lunch. Make one
estimate reasonable and one unreasonable. Choose the better
estimate and explain your choice.

Facts Practice ————————————————— KEY **NS 2.1**

Subtract.

1. 73 − 25   **2.** 94 − 61   **3.** 82 − 76

4. 58 − 19   **5.** 65 − 38   **6.** 40 − 17

Hands On: Metric Units of Mass

Choose the unit you would use to measure the mass of each. Write *g* or *kg*.

1. a ruler
_____

2. a computer printer
_____

3. a computer disk
_____

4. a tomato
_____

5. an envelope
_____

6. a bicycle
_____

Choose the better estimate

7. a book
1 g or 1 kg
_____

8. a peanut
1 g or 100 g
_____

9. a pair of boots
200 kg or 2 kg
_____

10. a scarf
60 g or 60 kg
_____

11. a car
800 g or 800 kg
_____

12. a bowling ball
70 g or 7 kg
_____

Test Practice

Circle the letter of the correct answer.

13. Which of the following would you measure using grams (*g*)?

   A a motorcycle

   B a table

   C a piece of paper

   D a stack of newspapers

14. Which of the following would you measure using kilograms (*kg*)?

   A a computer

   B a golf ball

   C an onion

   D a pair of gloves

Writing Math The mass of an apple is usually measured with grams. Suppose your teacher had a large paperweight shaped like an apple. Would you still use grams as the unit to measure its mass?

_____

_____

_____

Convert Metric Units

Problem of the Day ———————————————— MG 1.1

Phillipe measured the mass of a dictionary, a CD, and his dog. He recorded the measures in a chart. The measures are 90 g, 15 kg, and 2 kg. Which measure most likely belongs with which item?

Statistics, Data Analysis, and Probability Review KEY SDAP 1.2

Anna put 5 red cubes, 3 green cubes, and 2 blue cubes in a bag. She took out 1 cube without looking, recorded the color, and put the cube back. She repeated this 25 times. How many different outcomes does Anna's experiment have? Name them.

Number of the Day ———————————————— NS 1.0

1,000

Name some things that 1,000 can represent.

_____

_____

_____

Facts Practice ———————————————— KEY NS 2.2

Multiply.

1. 7×2 2. 9×5 3. 4×6

4. 8×8 5. 5×7 6. 9×3

Convert Metric Units

CA Standard
AF 1.4

**Choose the expression you would use to convert the units.
Then convert the units.**

1. the number of milliliters in 9 liters _____
   a. $9 \times 1{,}000$ b. $1{,}000 \div 9$

2. the number of meters in 400 centimeters _____
   a. 400×100 b. $400 \div 100$

3. the number of kilograms in 3,000 grams _____
   a. $3{,}000 \times 1{,}000$ b. $3{,}000 \div 1{,}000$

4. the number of centimeters in 80 meters _____
   a. 80×100 b. $100 \div 80$

5. the number of liters in 20,000 milliliters _____
   a. $20{,}000 \times 1{,}000$ b. $20{,}000 \div 1{,}000$

6. the number of grams in 19 kilograms _____
   a. $1{,}000 \div 19$ b. $19 \times 1{,}000$

7. the number of meters in 500 centimeters _____
   a. $500 \div 100$ b. 500×100

8. the number of liters in 50,000 milliliters _____
   a. $50{,}000 \times 1{,}000$ b. $50{,}000 \div 1{,}000$

Test Practice

Circle the letter of the correct answer.

9. Which of the following is used to find how many meters (*m*) are in 200 centimeters?

   A $200 \times 1{,}000$ c $200 \div 100$

   B $200 \div 1$ D 200×100

10. Which of the following is used to find how many kilograms (*kg*) are in 8,000 grams?

    A $8{,}000 \times 1$ c $1{,}000 \times 8{,}000$

    B $8{,}000 \div 1{,}000$ D $8{,}000 \div 100$

Writing Math Can a ruler be measured by more than one unit of metric measurement? Explain.

_____

_____

_____

Problem Solving: Field Trip

Problem of the Day ———————————— AF 1.4, MG 1.4

A melon weighs 3 kilograms. Write an expression that you
can use to find the mass of the melon in grams. Then find its
mass in grams.

Number Sense Review ———————————— KEY NS 2.3

What multiplication and division sentences are modeled by
this array?

Number of the Day ———————————— NS 3.1

$\frac{2}{3}$

Name two fractions that are equivalent to $\frac{2}{3}$. Draw pictures if you
need help.

_____

_____

_____

Facts Practice ———————————— NS 2.5

Divide.

1. $54 \div 6$ 2. $49 \div 7$ 3. $16 \div 2$

4. $32 \div 4$ 5. $20 \div 5$ 6. $81 \div 9$

Looking Ahead Activities

Next year, you will learn more about
problem-solving with whole numbers
and fractions, geometry, and data.
The Looking Ahead activities will
help you get ready.

Name _____ Date _____

Which Fractions Are the Same?

CA Standards
NS 3.1 prepares for
Gr. 4 NS 1.5, NS 1.6, NS 1.7

By yourself

Materials: two different-colored crayons

Shade each circle to represent the given fraction.

1.
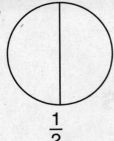
$\dfrac{1}{2}$

2.
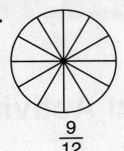
$\dfrac{9}{12}$

3.
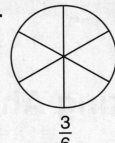
$\dfrac{3}{6}$

4.
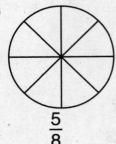
$\dfrac{5}{8}$

5.
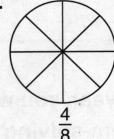
$\dfrac{3}{4}$

6.
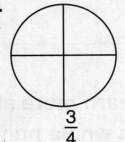
$\dfrac{4}{8}$

7.
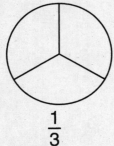
$\dfrac{1}{3}$

8.
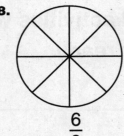
$\dfrac{6}{8}$

9.
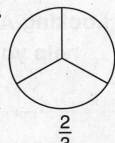
$\dfrac{2}{3}$

10. Find a group of circles that all show the same amount. Circle them with one color crayon. Write each fraction.

_____

11. Find another group of circles that all show the same amount. Circle them with another color crayon. Write each fraction.

_____

Objective: Construct concrete models of equivalent fractions.

Name _____   Date _____

Fractions on a Number Line

CA Standards
NS 3.1 prepares for
Gr. 4 **KEY** NS 1.9

With your partner

Materials: fraction tiles, paper strips

1. Use four $\boxed{\frac{1}{4}}$ fraction tiles. Place them in a row on a paper strip. Mark the end of each fraction piece on the paper strip.

2. Mark the strip below to show your fourths. Write these fractions in order in the parts:

   $\frac{1}{4}, \frac{2}{4}, \frac{3}{4}, \frac{4}{4}.$

   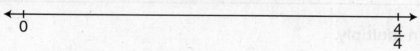

3. Make marks on the number line to show fourths. Label each mark with the correct fraction.

   $$\overset{\displaystyle 0}{\longleftarrow}\!\!+\!+\overset{\displaystyle \frac{4}{4}}{\longrightarrow}$$

   ____   ____   ____

4. Use eight $\boxed{\frac{1}{8}}$ fraction tiles. Place them in a row on a paper strip. Mark the end of each fraction piece on the paper strip.

5. Mark the strip below to show your eighths. Write these fractions in order in the parts:

   $\frac{1}{8}, \frac{2}{8}, \frac{3}{8}, \frac{4}{8}, \frac{5}{8}, \frac{6}{8}, \frac{7}{8}, \frac{8}{8}.$

   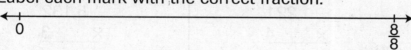

6. Make marks on the number line to show eighths. Label each mark with the correct fraction.

   $$\overset{\displaystyle 0}{\longleftarrow}\!\!+\!+\overset{\displaystyle \frac{8}{8}}{\longrightarrow}$$

   ___ ___ ___ ___ ___ ___ ___

Objective: Order fractions on a number line.

Name _____ Date _____

Multiplication

CA Standards
KEY NS 2.2, KEY NS 2.4
prepares for Gr. 4 KEY NS 3.3

By yourself

Multiply 2 × 1,324.

Multiply the ones.	Multiply the tens.	Multiply the hundreds.	Multiply the thousands.
2 × 4 = 8 ones	2 × 2 tens = 4 tens	2 × 3 hundreds = 6 hundreds	2 × 1 thousand = 2 thousands
1,324 × 2 ——— 8 └─8 ones	1,324 × 2 ——— 48 └─4 tens	1,324 × 2 ——— 648 └─6 hundreds	1,324 × 2 ——— 2,648 └─2 thousands

Estimate the product. Then multiply.

1. 2 × 2,141

Estimate: _____

2,141
× 2

2. 3 × 1,231

Estimate: _____

1,231
× 3

3. 4 × 5,122

Estimate: _____

5,122
× 4

4. 2 × 3,214

Estimate: _____

3,214
× 2

5. 4 × 1,221

Estimate: _____

1,221
× 4

6. 3 × 5,132

Estimate: _____

5,132
× 3

Objective: Multiply multidigit numbers.

Division

CA Standards
KEY NS 2.3, NS 2.5 prepares
for Gr. 4 KEY NS 3.4

Divide 135 ÷ 3.

By yourself

Try to divide the hundreds.
 	
3)135
 	
↑
 	
1 hundred needs to be regrouped as 10 tens.
	Divide the tens. Subtract.
	
	  4
	3)135 ←—13 tens ÷ 3
	− 12
	———
	  1
		Bring down the ones. Divide the ones. Subtract.
		
		  45
		3)135 Bring down
		− 12↓ 5 ones.
		———
		  15 ←—15 ones ÷ 3
		− 15
		———
		   0

Estimate the quotient. Then divide.
Multiply to check your answer.

1. 125 ÷ 5

Estimate: _____

5)125

Check your answer.
Multiply.

2. 112 ÷ 4

Estimate: _____

4)112

Check your answer.
Multiply.

3. 162 ÷ 3

Estimate: _____

3)162

Check your answer.
Multiply.

Objective: Divide a multidigit number by a one-digit number.

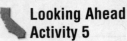
Rounding Numbers Game

CA Standards
NS 1.4, prepares for
Gr. 4 **KEY** NS 1.3, **KEY** NS 1.4

With your partner

Materials: bag and number
cards 1–9

- Place number cards labeled 1 though 9 in a bag.

- Draw 3 number cards from the bag without looking.

- With your partner, arrange the cards to find two or more numbers that round to the same 100.

- Before repeating the activity, place the cards back in the bag.

Numbers Drawn	Can Two or More Numbers Round to the Same 100?	If So, Which Numbers?

How can you determine if two or more numbers can round to the same 100?

_____

_____

_____

Objective: Round whole numbers to the nearest hundred.

What Did I Measure?

Use objects in your classroom.

- Measure the length and the width of at least two objects in inches or feet using a ruler or yardstick.

- On an index card, record the length, the width, and a word that describes the object such as its color or shape.

- Use a separate index card for each object.

- On the back, write the name of the object you are describing.

CA Standards
MG 1.1 prepares for
Gr. 4 MG 1.4

With a small group

Materials: paper, index cards, rulers, yardsticks, and classroom objects

Front of Card

Length	Width	Description Word

Back of Card

Name of Object

- Now, in groups, try to guess what object is being described.

- Write your guess on a piece of paper.

- After talking about it with your group, check your answer by looking on the back of the index card. Continue until you go through all the cards.

How many objects did your group guess correctly?

Objective: Estimate and measure lengths using standard units.

Name _____ Date _____

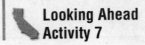
Find the Area

Find classroom items with one flat surface that can fit onto a piece of paper. Such objects are sticky notes, rulers, erasers, and so forth. Write down the name of the object and estimate its area.

CA Standards
KEY MG 1.2 prepares for
Gr. 4 MG 1.1, MG 1.2

By yourself

Materials: grid paper, classroom objects

Remember that **area** is the measure of the amount of space needed to cover the inside of a shape. Area is measured in **square units.** Square units can be square inches, square feet, square yards, square centimeters, or any other unit of length squared.

For this activity you will

• use each square on the grid as a unit of measurement.

• measure the object by placing it on grid paper and outlining the object with a pencil.

• count the squares to find the actual area.

• record this information in the chart.

Object	Estimate	Measured Area

Objective: Find the area of a two-dimensional surface.

Looking Ahead Activity

7

Measure Perimeter

CA Standards
MG 1.1 prepares for
Gr. 4 MG 1.3, MG 1.4

With a small group

Materials: ruler,
yardstick, and tape
measure

Perimeter is the distance around a shape or figure. You can use different units of measure to measure perimeter.

For small objects, you can use inches.

For large objects, you can use feet or yards.

Use rulers and yardsticks when you want to measure straight lines. To measure round or curved shapes, use a tape measure.

With a small group, measure the perimeter of several objects in the classroom using a ruler, yardstick, or tape measure. Record the name of the object and the perimeter.

Object	Perimeter
1.	
2.	
3.	
4.	
5.	
6.	
7.	
8.	

Compare your results with other groups.

What is the shortcut for finding the perimeter of a rectangular object?

_____

Objective: Find the perimeter of a shape.

Use Tools to Measure

For this activity you will

CA Standards
MG 1.1 prepares for
Gr. 4 MR 3.2

With your partner

Materials: classroom objects

- look at what you have to measure for each object listed in the chart.

- choose the best tool to measure the object.

- record the tool in the chart.

	Object	Measure	Tool
1.	book	length	_____
2.	milk carton	capacity	_____
3.	stapler	weight	_____
4.	marker	mass	_____
5.	chalk board 4 + 4 = 8	length	_____

Change the units

6. A quart carton of milk = _____ cups

7. A 1 lb box of pasta = _____ oz

8. A 2 kg package of flour = _____ g

9. A 5 yd long rug = _____ ft

1 foot = 12 inches
1 yard = 3 feet
1 pint = 2 cups
1 quart = 4 cups
1 pound = 16 ounces
1 kilogram = 1,000 grams

Objectives: Choose the appropriate tool to measure length, liquid volume, weight, and mass of given objects. Convert units.

Name _____ Date _____

What Is the Angle?

CA Standards
MG 2.4 prepares for Gr. 4
MG 3.5

With your partner

Use the clocks. Tell whether the angle is a right angle, greater than a right angle, or less than a right angle.

1.

_____

2.

_____

3.

_____

4.

_____

5.

_____

6.

_____

Objective: Identify angles that are less than, greater than, or equal to a right angle.

Polygons

KEY MG 2.2 prepares for
Gr. 4 MG 3.7

By yourself

A **polygon** is a flat, closed figure made up of
3 or more sides.

Look at the polygon. Find triangles in the polygon.

Trace the triangles in the polygon. Label each triangle with the
kind of triangle it is: equilateral, isosceles, right, scalene.

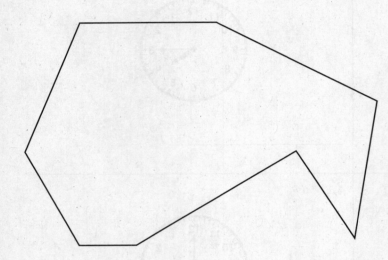

Draw a design that includes several polygons.

**Include a triangle, a quadrilateral, a pentagon, a hexagon, and
an octagon.**

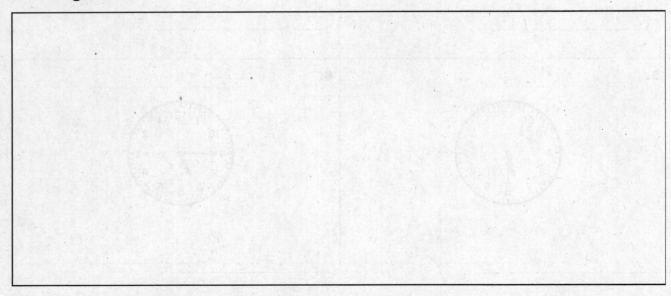

Objective: Describe and make polygons. Identify shapes within polygons.

Name _____   Date _____

Quadrilaterals

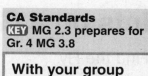
CA Standards
KEY MG 2.3 prepares for
Gr. 4 MG 3.8

A **quadrilateral** is a flat, closed figure that has 4 sides and 4 angles.

Here are some special quadrilaterals.

With your group
Materials: straws, scissors, clay

square	**rectangle**	**parallelogram**	**rhombus**
• all four sides have the same length • has 4 right angles	• opposite sides are parallel • has 4 right angles	• opposite sides are parallel • opposite sides are the same length	• opposite sides are parallel • all 4 sides are the same length

Use straws. Make quadrilaterals.
Show a parallelogram, square, rectangle, and rhombus.
Draw your quadrilaterals.

square	**rectangle**
parallelogram	**rhombus**

Objective: Identify attributes of quadrilaterals.

Points on a Grid

CA Standards
MR 2.0 prepares for
Gr. 4 KEY MG 2.0

With your partner

Play Find the Fly.

Directions

• Each of you marks a fly on one point of your grid.

• Take turns naming coordinates where you think your partner's fly is located.

• Your partner tells whether or not you are correct.

• Keep guessing. The first player to find the other player's fly wins!

Name _____

Fly Location _____

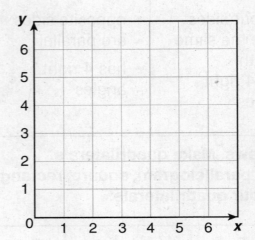

Objective: Locate and draw points on a coordinate grid.

Name _____ Date _____

Build Solid Shapes

CA Standards
MG 2.5 prepares for
Gr. 4 MG 3.6

With your group

Materials: toothpicks, mini marshmallows or clay

Here are some solid shapes.

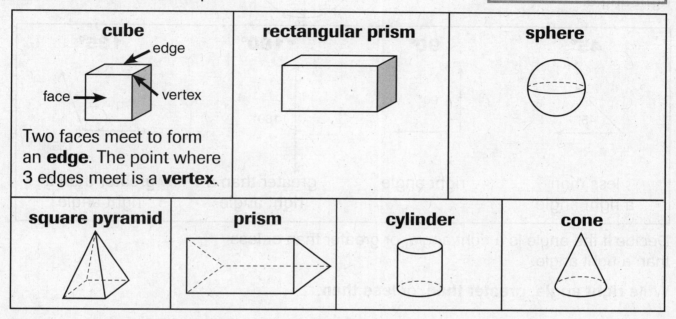

Use toothpicks as edges. Use marshmallows
as vertices. Make each solid figure.
Draw your model.

cube	rectangular solid
pyramid	**prism**

Objective: Identify, describe, and make solid figures.

Find Angles

An angle is measured in units called degrees (°). There are 360 degrees in a circle. A 90-degree angle is a right angle.

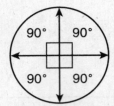

CA Standards
MG 2.4 prepares for
Gr. 4 MG 3.1

With your partner

Materials: index card

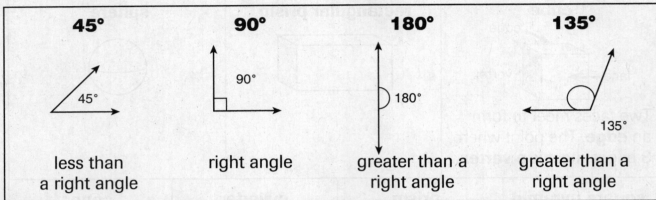

45°	**90°**	**180°**	**135°**
less than a right angle	right angle	greater than a right angle	greater than a right angle

Decide if the angle is a right angle, or greater than or less than a right angle.

Write **right angle**, **greater than**, or **less than**.

1.

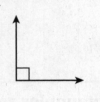

_____

2.

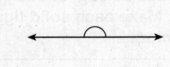

_____

3.

_____

4.

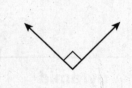

_____

5. Find an example of a right angle in your classroom. What is your example?

_____

Objective: Identify right angles. Identify whether angles are greater or less than a right angle.

Name _____ Date _____

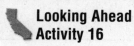

**Looking Ahead
Activity 16**

Probability

CA Standards
SDAP 1.1 prepares for
Gr. 4 SDAP 2.0

By yourself

An event that will happen is a **certain** event.
An event that probably will happen is a **likely** event.
An event that probably will not happen is an **unlikely** event.
An event that will never happen is an **impossible** event.

Write **certain, likely, unlikely,** or **impossible**.

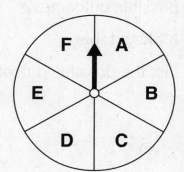

1. It is _____ that a spin will land on D.

2. It is _____ that a spin will land on a consonant.

3. It is _____ that a spin will land on G.

4. It is _____ that a spin will land on a letter
   or a line.

Use the spinner above. Write the probability in fraction form.

5. A spin landing on a vowel

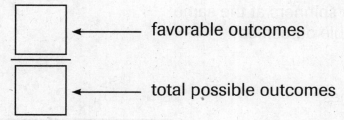

6. A spin landing on a consonant

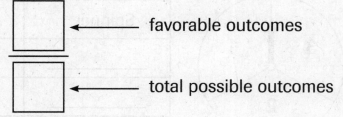

7. A spin landing on B

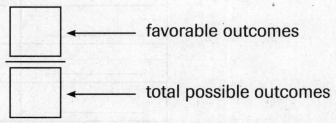

Objective: Determine if an event is certain, likely, unlikely, or impossible.
Name the probability in a fraction.

Looking Ahead Activity
Copyright © Houghton Mifflin Company. All rights reserved.

16

Recording Outcomes

CA Standards
KEY SDAP 1.2 prepares
for Gr. 4 SDAP 2.1

By yourself

If you toss two pennies, what are the possible outcomes?

Make a table.

List the possible outcomes.

Possible Outcomes	
Coin 1	Coin 2
_____	_____
_____	_____
_____	_____
_____	_____

If you spin both of these spinners at the same time, what are the possible outcomes?

Make a table.

List the possible outcomes.

Spinner 1

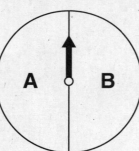

Spinner 2

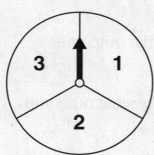

Possible Outcomes	
Spinner 1	Spinner 2
_____	_____
_____	_____
_____	_____
_____	_____
_____	_____
_____	_____

Objective: Record the possible outcomes for a simple event using tables and grids.

Name _____ Date _____

Make Predictions

Spin both spinners. Add the two numbers.
The sum is the outcome. Record the outcome.
Spin 18 times.

CA Standards
SDAP 1.4 prepares for
Gr. 4 SDAP 2.0

With your partner

Materials: paper clip, pencil

Spinner 1

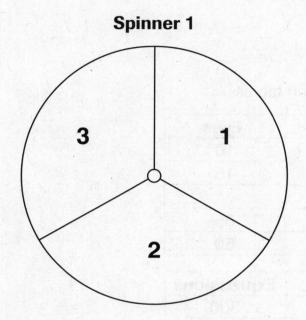

Spinner 2

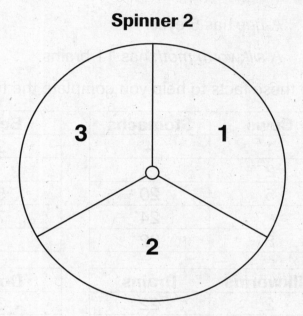

Make a line plot to record the outcome. Draw an X above the sum.

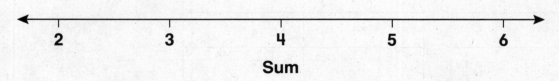

Sum

Use your results above. Predict the outcome of 18 more spins.

_____

_____

Objective: Use the results of probability experiments to predict future events.

Tables of Unusual Facts

CA Standards
KEY SDAP 1.3 prepares for
Gr. 4 SDAP 1.1

With a small group

Here are some interesting animal facts.

A *cow* has 4 stomachs.

A *dog* has about 100 different facial expressions.

A *bee* has 5 eyes.

A *silkworm moth* has 11 brains.

Use these facts to help you complete the function tables.

Cows	Stomachs
1	4
2	
5	20
	24
8	32

Bees	Eyes
2	10
	15
5	
7	35
	50

Silkworms	Brains
2	22
4	44
5	
	77
9	

Dogs	Expressions
3	300
5	
6	600
8	800
	1,200

Find 2 more interesting animal facts and write your own function tables.

Objective: Generate a table of paired numbers based on a real-life situation.

Read a Graph

CA Standards
KEY SDAP 1.3 prepares for
Gr. 4 SDAP 1.1

With your partner

A **bar graph** compares data by using bars of different lengths. The bar graph shows the top speeds of animals.

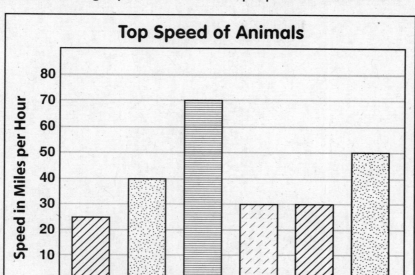

Use the bar graph to answer the questions.

1. Which animal has the greatest top speed?

_____

2. Which animal has the least top speed?

_____

3. How many miles per hour faster is a zebra than a cat? _____

4. Which animal has a top speed of 25 miles per hour?

_____

5. What is the top speed of a lion?

_____

6. Which two animals have the same top speed?

_____

Objective: Interpret information from bar graphs.